ADHD Explained: What Every Parent Needs to Know

Dr. Nekeshia Hammond

Legal and Medical Disclaimers: Although Dr. Nekeshia Hammond is a licensed psychologist, this book is a work of her opinions and not necessarily guaranteed facts. Many of these opinions are backed up by statistics, studies and mental health tests, however, this book has been written for entertainment purposes and should not be looked in any other manner than this. Are there a lot of facts and resources in this book? Absolutely, but never feel that you have to take the ideas and opinions in this book and go against your own judgment. Feel free to consult your own physicians, psychologists, counselors, religious leaders, etc... and form your own opinions.

Although the author has made every effort to ensure that the information in this book was correct at press time, the author does not assume and does hereby disclaim any liability to any party for any loss, damage, or disruption caused by errors or omissions, whether such errors or omissions result from negligence, accident, or any other cause.

This book is not intended as a substitute for the advice of a mental or other health professional. The reader should regularly consult a professional in matters relating to his/her mental or emotional health and/or the mental or emotional health of their child/children and particularly with respect to any symptoms that may require diagnosis or medical attention. The information in this book is meant to supplement, not replace, proper counseling and/or guidance.

Cover design **by Alex Rodriguez, YMMYMarketing.com**
Editing and interior design **by Eli Gonzalez, TheGhostPublishing.com**

ADHD Explained: What Every Parent Needs to Know
By, Dr. Nekeshia Hammond

Publisher: **Hammond Psychology Press** (HammondPsychologyPress.com)
ISBN: 978-0-692-05967-8

Thank you!

This book is dedicated to my favorite little boy on the planet, Laurence, my first-born son. Thank you for being such a kind boy and motivating mommy to help children and families, my sweet son.

Contents

Introduction

Ever since I was 7 years old, I knew that I wanted to make a difference in the lives of children and families. I thought, *what could be better?* I didn't know then exactly how I could make a difference. I just felt I had to.

As I grew, I figured there were myriad ways I could help families; I could be a doctor, a dietician, a teacher or a social worker. There are plenty of options for someone who truly wants to help others. As I got to the point in my life when I had to decide what do with the rest of it, I had narrowed it down. I would be a Psychologist and help children with special needs.

I have been blessed to provide psychological evaluations for children to assess for ADHD and other conditions for over a decade, and I absolutely love what I do! To watch a family thrive while understanding that their child can be successful in life, despite having ADHD, has been incredibly fulfilling.

In completing psychological evaluations to help parents become certain whether their child has

ADHD, and, if so, what to do about it, I have seen the lives of families change dramatically. Parents have been able to learn how best to approach their child, adjust their expectations, and love their child for their unique qualities. With comprehensive psychological evaluations, parents can understand their child in whole: socially, emotionally, behaviorally, intellectually, and overall how their child functions. Parents with this valuable information about their child can truly empower their child to function in a stressful world. Learning how to navigate through the diagnosis of ADHD, understanding the education system, and becoming aware of the parenting challenges are all a part of the journey that parents of a child with ADHD face.

As a psychologist specializing in children and teens, I've been so blessed to work with hundreds of youth with ADHD at this point in my career. I've seen children that were misdiagnosed with ADHD while performing second opinion evaluations. I've witnessed children that had ADHD and another condition left unaddressed (such as a learning disability or behavioral issue) until a comprehensive psychological evaluation. But overall, I'm so fortunate to work with parents that found hope and the proper education to advocate for their children and help their children be successful, healthy, and productive individuals. My passion has always been to help children and families, so it has been my honor to consult with many media outlets (radio, television, and magazine) throughout the country to advocate for children's mental health. I also consider myself fortunate to have been invited to speak at events throughout the country about ways to help children be emotionally healthy.

My hope for this book is that parents understand how to help their child with ADHD and also nurture themselves as caregivers. I want for all parents struggling with this idea of what society tells them ADHD is (and is not) to become clear about the facts. I would love for parents to be empowered with knowledge and education about how to help their child. It is my hope that parents also remember the importance of self-care through the parenting journey.

Not every day will be easy, but with the proper tools and resources, a parent can learn to navigate through these times. With the establishment of a support system and a team approach, you can learn to collaborate with others to produce the best outcome for your child. The number one response that I get when I ask parents what they want for their child is for their child to be happy. Here's to happy, healthy, and productive children!

And to the happiness, health, and productivity of their parents!

Chapter 1

Meet Suzie

Suzie couldn't explain why. Her teacher had told her several times to stop fidgeting and she tried, she really did. She just, couldn't.

"Do you have ants in your pants or something?" Mrs. Smith chided good-naturedly, forgetting how brutally eight-year-olds can tease one another. While at recess later in the day, even Suzie's bestest friends joined with the other kids in making fun of her. That afternoon, Suzie was put in timeout for not being able to keep from shaking her legs.

A few weeks and a few more timeouts later, Suzie had become the teacher's "bad kid in class." Mrs. Smith asked to meet with her parents, who were far too busy to meet with her; but they made the time because they also thought Suzie was, at times, too distracted or "energetic."

She couldn't pay attention long enough. She couldn't stand still in line. She couldn't stop herself from blurting out an answer when she hadn't been called on. She couldn't go to sleep when it was bed time. She couldn't seem to get many things right.

Two years later, after being labeled a troubled kid, Suzie had only one friend in school. Her world diminished to include only those closest to her. She wanted to have more friends, she wanted to be invited to birthday parties, she wanted to be accepted, she wanted to be loved – she wanted to behave... she, just... couldn't – and she couldn't explain why.

Why am I different?

Why do I keep making my parents so sad?

Why is everyone against me?

What is wrong with me?

Am I bad?

Her parents changed her diet, put her in timeouts, took away her favorite toys, promised her more goodies if she would behave, but nothing changed. She heard her parents arguing about her, each one blaming the other on why she wouldn't listen. She ran to the living room to get them to stop fighting. She wanted to promise them she'd be good, but before she could, her dad stomped out of the house.

What is wrong with me? Am I bad? Maybe I'm broken.

My name is Dr. Nekeshia Hammond, I help boys and girls like Suzie, and their parents. Most people, including some "professionals" don't understand what ADHD is and how to best treat the wonderful people inflicted by it.

I'm here to help.

Chapter 2

Understanding ADHD

Your child may have been diagnosed with ADHD or you may believe that your child has ADHD. Many parents that I've met don't realize that there are actually three types of ADHD in what's called the Diagnostic Statistical Manual, 5th Edition (DSM-5), a book used in the field of psychiatry that includes diagnoses and criteria for all psychiatric disorders.

The three types of ADHD are:

- ADHD, Hyperactive/Impulsive Presentation (mostly hyperactive and impulsive symptoms)
- ADHD Inattentive Presentation (mostly inattention symptoms)
- ADHD Combined Presentation (most commonly diagnosed with both inattentive and hyperactive and impulsive symptoms.)

To learn more about the full criteria for ADHD, you can check out the CDC website[1]. Please note that the CDC Resources are provided solely to increase your awareness, so please do not attempt to "diagnose" your child, but rather follow up with a professional if you have concerns.

Is ADHD over-diagnosed?

A question that many parents have asked me is whether ADHD is an over-diagnosed condition. The answer is, unfortunately, a resounding YES. The reason? There are many theories as to why ADHD is over-diagnosed. For starters, it is true that in today's age we are more aware of the actual signs and symptoms that look like ADHD. Even though children may not have been diagnosed with ADHD in years past, it doesn't mean that they didn't have the symptoms, we just didn't have the clinical name. My professional opinion is that one of the reasons why ADHD is over-diagnosed is that many evaluations lack comprehensiveness. Conducting evaluations using a quick questionnaire and screener may, sometimes,

There are numerous individuals diagnosed with ADHD in childhood and those individuals go on to live happy, successful, and productive lives.

be accurate, but the reality is that ADHD is often diagnosed when there is really something else going on with the child, such as depression, anxiety, a learning disability, trauma, or a strong reaction to a recent stressful event in the family. In essence, there are so many things that mimic the ADHD symptoms.

The other issue is that in 2013, the criteria for the DSM-5 changed and the symptoms of ADHD may now be considered to be present *before 12 years of age* (in years past, it was seven years old).

Does that mean that younger children did not have ADHD before 2013? Of course, not; but, it is now easier to diagnose children at younger ages (and hopefully with greater accuracy), but at the same time the numbers will have increased because of the change of diagnostic classification.

Here are a few problems with the misdiagnosis of ADHD:

- Children being overmedicated

  Who wants to put their child on medication when they don't need it? No one!

- Treating the wrong thing

  When ADHD is misdiagnosed, this results in children potentially consuming medications unnecessarily. Secondly, when you treat the wrong condition, you are not working to resolve the problem. For instance, let's say that 'Suzie' is treated for ADHD, which she doesn't have, instead of a learning disability, which she does have. Chances are that she will still struggle in school, be frustrated in school, and may have behavioral issues that are not addressed, simply because she's struggling with an undiagnosed learning disability. I have, unfortunately, witnessed this scenario often.

• Not treating the entire issue

Finally, there is the circumstance where a child really does have ADHD, but there is also another factor contributing to their overall picture, such as anxiety. So, what happens then? ADHD often becomes the primary focus. A disproportionate amount of energy is then invested in ADHD treatment, but the child still has symptoms that "look like" ADHD, but are actually rooted in anxious feelings.

These scenarios may sound familiar. You may be confident that your child was properly evaluated; but if not, in Chapters 3 and 4, I'll discuss what a proper evaluation should look like. There may be times when you want a second opinion to evaluate the diagnosis, or simply to learn more details about your child (like their learning strengths or if any other issue is affecting their functioning). Second opinion evaluations can often provide more detailed information.

The label of ADHD

Another issue that is concerning to parents is the idea of a "label" of ADHD. What does this mean for your child? Yes, it is true that a diagnosis of ADHD is, technically speaking, a "label." The reality is, however, that there are both pros and cons to this label.

Here are some of the benefits of having an ADHD diagnosis:

- An ADHD diagnosis helps a medical team understand the symptoms; providing for treatment opportunities.

- Many school systems will recognize the diagnosis and understand what services may need to be provided.

- A diagnosis can help parents understand what the condition means.

In the world of physical health, a condition like diabetes, high blood pressure, a heart issue, etc. is a diagnostic "label" which allows a medical team to know what the issue is that they are dealing with and how best to treat it. Similarly, a proper diagnosis of ADHD means that the treatment team can best work on ways to appropriately treat the condition, with research-backed methods to best help your child. The way many school systems are currently instituted, the "label" of ADHD is necessary in order to receive the appropriate educational services or accommodations to help your child. Unfortunately, I have seen way too many children fail to receive the help they needed in the school system because they did not have the documentation of their ADHD symptoms for school purposes. Lastly, it also helps as a parent to know what the condition is that your child has so that you can do your own research to best help your child at home and know the next steps to providing your child with the help that they need.

Some of the cons of having a label of ADHD are:

- Stereotypes and people unnecessarily judging your child
- Having to explain the diagnosis to others
- A sense of guilt that you may have as a parent
- That your child may have a negative interpretation of the label
- The stigma of needing mental health help.

Unfortunately, the world still has many stereotypes about what ADHD is and what it isn't. There are numerous individuals diagnosed with ADHD in childhood and those individuals go on to live happy, successful, and productive lives. According to the Centers for Disease Control, "Approximately 11% of children 4-17 years of age (6.4 million) have ever been diagnosed with ADHD according to parent report from 2011-12," but research also shows that with treatment, many of these children can be successful.[2]

When you decide to discuss your child's ADHD diagnosis with a friend, family member, colleague, teacher, or another individual, you may hear comments like "ADHD is not real," "Yup, everyone is diagnosed with ADHD, nowadays," "Lemme guess, they want to put your kid on medication?" or some other variation of those unsupportive comments.

In Chapter 8, I'll discuss ways to help you find your support network to get through those tough comments. For now, just recognize that many parents feel a sense of guilt when they learn of their child's diagnosis. If you don't feel a sense of guilt, then congratulations! But, if you do feel guilt, please understand that this is normal and that there are ways to move beyond it to embark on the journey of being the best parent for your child.

> *The most important thing to recognize is that a proper evaluation is key...*

Additionally, your child's reaction is important, as well. Some children do not do well with the new diagnosis of ADHD, but there are many resources available to help them deal with this diagnosis. The reality is if your child was diagnosed with the flu, you probably wouldn't think twice about revealing it, but when your child is diagnosed with ADHD, you may be much more reluctant to discuss it. It's unfortunate, but there is still a large stigma associated with needing mental health help. Thank you, again, for taking the time to read this book, because it means that you are not allowing this stigma to hinder you on your journey. It is my strongest hope that we continue as a society in the journey to eradicate the stigma associated with mental health treatment.

What are the causes of ADHD?

- Heredity

  Much of the research currently points to heredity as one of the causes of ADHD (see more information from the Mayo Clinic).[3] There have been many family studies that have shown a higher link of ADHD in siblings and other family connections.

- Brain structure

  Some research studies have found that individuals with ADHD have different brain structure, such as smaller brain structures.[4]

- Pregnancy behaviors

  One study looked at pregnancy behaviors, such as the use of amphetamines as a cause for ADHD, but there are still studies ongoing.[5] Poor diet, drug/alcohol use and smoking during pregnancy have also been linked to ADHD.

  Overall, there is a lot more research that needs to be done in the field of ADHD to determine causal factors. To gather more information about causes linked to ADHD, you can check out Healthline's article on this topic.[6]

What does not cause ADHD?

Poor parenting, excessive video games, too much television, and food are many times thought to cause ADHD. There have been many research studies that have shown that those factors do not cause ADHD. You may be wondering about the food issue, however. While many studies have not shown that excessive sugar causes ADHD, it is obviously still a great idea to limit sugar intake, especially if you feel it is contributing to hyperactivity in your child. Also, some parents have reported success with a change in diet for ADHD symptoms. While this is not documented by a large body of research, remember to do what works best for your child, but be careful of a mindset of a "cure" versus a mindset of "control" for their symptoms.

Common Myths

Some of the common myths that I have heard from parents and children are the following:

"If you have ADHD, you can't be successful in school"

"It's all my fault"

"My kids with ADHD won't do well in life"

"ADHD means kids will be difficult"

"You can't ever get better with ADHD"

While there are many myths, when looking at the outcome studies for ADHD, the reality is that ADHD is treatable. According to the Journal of Attention Disorders, children treated for ADHD did better academically than those untreated.[7] The most important thing to recognize is that a proper evaluation is key, school accommodations are generally a must, home interventions can work great, and there is a source of support from mental health and other health professionals. It may take a team approach (see Chapter 13 for building a team), but your child may be successful given the advocacy and sufficient dedication to your family journey.

Understanding ADHD

In our office, we teach the five steps to understanding ADHD:

1) Consultation

Consultation comes in many forms. The first form of consultation is to visit a physician for your child to rule out whether there are any medical conditions that might be affecting your child which look like ADHD symptoms. There are a lot of physical symptoms that can affect children that could cause them to have problems in school, such as, difficulty concentrating, problems with hyperactivity, or behavioral issues. The other part of a consultation is to visit a psychologist to evaluate your child. During the initial consultation, you can provide the mental health professional detailed and thorough information about your child. This evaluation will look at a variety of factors that affect your child.

2) Evaluation

The next step is evaluation, which may take the form of a psychological or neuropsychological evaluation. There are many variations of these evaluations. But the most important thing to remember is that you want a comprehensive evaluation, not something that's going to take only five to 10 minutes to decide whether your child has ADHD, and what your next steps should be. While I greatly respect the medical profession, some of the problems that are seen at times are where determinations are being made in five to 10 minutes for medications and for placement in school and what type of interventions for a child with ADHD. Spending only five to 10 minutes to make such important decisions, ultimately affecting a child's entire life can really be problematic and it has its flaws. So, a way to avoid this is to get your child a psychological evaluation or a neuropsychological evaluation, which is a much more comprehensive process.

3) Confirmation

The third step in the process of understanding your child with ADHD is what I call confirmation, where you determine whether your child has ADHD. This step is very important for a couple of reasons. Number one, you can have peace of mind as a parent to know with certainty whether or not your child has ADHD. So many parents frequently ask me the question, "Does my child have ADHD?" Sadly, I also have seen many parents remain in anguish for years due to the stigma of mental health not receive an evaluation earlier. You may also have been blaming yourself for behavioral symptoms, but do not blame yourself! ADHD is not your fault.

I have found that, when the answer is received and there is confirmation of an ADHD diagnosis, a couple different reactions come into play. If you learn that your child has ADHD, be prepared for various reactions within yourself. You might actually feel relieved. Many parents say, "Thank you for allowing me to understand my child better now so that I know what to do." I have some parents that feel a sense of joy because they understand better now what is going on with their child.

There are many parents that have suspected for years or maybe have had a teacher that told them when their child was in first grade and second grade and now it's third grade and the symptoms aren't getting better. Other parents have said, "Well, I saw what I saw, but I thought my child would just grow out of it. I thought it was a phase." One of the great things about the confirmation stage is that there is no wrong or right way to feel. Another feeling may be confusion and you may be wondering what you should do next for your child. Or, you might be sad because your child has just been diagnosed with a mental health condition.

The confirmation stage, though, is really an opportunity though for you to learn. Begin to say to yourself, "Yes, my child has ADHD and I am determined to be an advocate for them. I am determined to learn everything that I can for my child to make their life better." Should you need extra support within yourself, please know that you deserve to get the support that you need. Remember that there could be so many things that look like

ADHD, which is why it is critical for you to make sure that you have your thorough evaluation to know with certainty whether your child has ADHD or not.

4) Intervention

The next step in the process is intervention. The intervention process gives you the opportunity to take the next steps and get your child the help that they need. Imagine for a minute what it was like when your child was exhibiting behaviors like hyperactivity, impulsivity, forgetting things at home and losing their homework, being disorganized, having a messy desk, having problems focusing on what the teacher was saying when they were daydreaming all day, when your child was so talkative because they had a hard time focusing, when they were distracted at home when there were chores that needed to be done, and they often forgot the tasks asked of them. Imagine all of those pieces of the puzzle, but you didn't know what that all meant. Then you learned that this is ADHD. Now you know how to help.

The great thing about ADHD is that it is a very well-researched condition and there is quite a range of interventions available to help. Some interventions including medication, and, in some cases, different type of therapies.

Examples of interventions are:

- Individual therapy (play therapy if your child is younger)

- Family therapy (if you're looking to really work on the communication skills of your family and how to communicate now that you do know that your child has ADHD)
- Parenting sessions for you to understand more about ADHD and how to parent your ADHD child
- Social skills training therapy sessions.

Your child may be struggling socially because other peers have a difficult time with their level of hyperactivity or impulsivity, or they have a hard time transitioning to going outside for recess, for instance. They may have a hard time transitioning from a large to a small group in class, or vice-versa; or, they may just have a hard time making friends in general because of behavioral issues or whatever the issue may be. Social skills training is another opportunity as far as an intervention. There are alternative types of interventions or alternative treatments that some families have found helpful. Now, I do want to preface this by saying that a lot of research regarding many of the alternative treatments has not shown a cure, but there can be some relief of some of the symptoms. So, that may be something that you can look into, but there are many different types of interventions. Many families have found a combination of interventions to be quite helpful for their child. There are also interventions that you can do in the home setting, the school setting, and in the employment setting for teens.

5) Collaboration

The fifth stage of understanding your child with ADHD is collaborating with other professionals. You will need to work together with so many different professionals throughout your parenting journey that it is vital for you to understand the power of collaboration and how collaboration can make such a difference for your child and to potentially change their life for the better. Collaboration is about having a "team" mentality and remembering that you do not have to solve all of your child's issues by yourself. You know your child best and one of your responsibilities is to explain your child's needs to others, especially because not every child with ADHD has the same issues. I trust that you will continue the process of learning about ADHD and utilize the references section of the book to learn more.

Make a commitment to the collaboration process. Although it may be frustrating at times, it is best to educate individuals and do your part in this process. We all have responsibilities in raising a child with ADHD. It's not just the parents' role. It's the teachers' role. It's the coaches' responsibility. It's the intervention specialists' responsibility. Everyone has a responsibility to this child and everyone needs to do their part.

If you were asked to provide certain paperwork, make sure to do that in a timely manner. Do the best that you can to provide the report card to assess the grades. Get the bloodwork completed to aid with the psychological evaluation. Attend your therapy sessions and medical appointments for your child. Ask questions. It's all about you doing your part and collaborating with others.

Another thing to help the process of collaboration is to think of it as long-term. While some children only have ADHD symptoms in their childhood years, for some children with ADHD, they will have it into their teen years; and, for some, throughout their lifetime. Sometimes it is difficult to understand which category they will necessarily be in, but the most important thing is for you to think of collaboration as long-term. Remember, this is a team approach to make sure that your child has the opportunities to be successful.

Now that you've learned about the five steps in the process of understanding your child with ADHD (consultation, evaluation, confirmation, intervention, and collaboration), the next thing that you need to do is to take action after you read this book.

Chapter 3

Start with
the Pediatrician

You may be reading this book because your child has already been diagnosed with ADHD, or perhaps you are thinking that they may have symptoms of ADHD, but they have not been formally diagnosed. Either way, this chapter is for you. If you haven't already, one of the first steps to take is to start with a pediatrician or your family physician.

Other medical health conditions

Sometimes ADHD can mimic physical health conditions, so it's important to receive a comprehensive physical examination to see if there are any medical conditions that may be impacting your child's functioning. I have heard stories of patients that have reported back that their physicians told them that their child had anemia, blood sugar regulation problems, thyroid issues, vitamin deficiencies, and a host of other conditions that can "look like" ADHD for a child's behavior.

Another thing to keep in mind is that the age of your child and their hormones may play a role in the diagnosis of ADHD. Talk to your doctor about any concerns of hormonal imbalances to see if supplements might be necessary to get your child back on track. Hormonal issues can affect the behavior of your child and

Many conditions look like ADHD, so get a physical check-up.

you may find that a hormonal evaluation is necessary. Infections can also affect a child's attention, concentration, hyperactivity, impulsivity, and other factors associated with ADHD.

There are many more medical health conditions that can appear to be ADHD, so consult with your family health physician so that they can utilize their expertise and ensure that there are no other issues contributing to your child's health.

Hearing and vision

Hearing and vision screenings are also vital. Often, children are simply struggling to see or hear information in class, and this sensory impairment has caused frustration and led to behavioral issues and attention problems. Thus, be sure that your child's hearing and vision are intact so that they are the most productive students in their classroom and at home.

ADHD screenings

Pediatricians may often do ADHD screenings, such as a parent and teacher questionnaire. While, by some standards, this may be sufficient to diagnose ADHD, recognize that some children need more comprehensive evaluations to assess their overall strengths and limitations. See Chapter 4 for what a detailed psychological evaluation entails.

Referrals

Your family care physician is often a great resource to get the follow-up referrals you will need for a child diagnosed with ADHD (or suspected of having ADHD). You may need to follow up to receive a referral for a comprehensive psychological evaluation. This evaluation can help to provide your pediatrician with additional information.

If your child has already been diagnosed with ADHD, your physician may be helpful in providing suggestions for mental health professionals so you can begin counseling. (Various forms of counseling will be explained in Chapter 9.) Many parents can also learn skills that can help a child with ADHD in the home setting, and the child can learn behavioral techniques for self-control and reducing impulsivity.

Another referral your pediatrician may give you, if necessary, is a referral to a neurologist. A neurologist is a specialist who treats diseases of the nervous system. A neuropsychologist is another referral you may receive (Chapter 4 talks about psychological and neuropsychological evaluations).

There are other needs that your child may have, and the pediatrician can also help to direct you to these specialists. Your child may have physical limitations; thus, the pediatrician may send you to a physical therapist. An occupational therapist may also be necessary if there are motor limitations. If your child is struggling with speech and/or language problems, a speech-language evaluation may also be necessary. Perhaps your child has significant developmental delays (walking, talking, toilet training, etc.), a developmental pediatrician may also be necessary.

Overall, your family physician can be a valuable resource to direct you to the specialists you need to get the answers you are searching for with your child. Remember, the more detailed information you receive about your child, the more you can understand about your child and learn ways to help them best. In the next chapter, you will learn about psychological and neuropsychological evaluations.

Chapter 4

Psychological and Neuropsychological Evaluations

By now you may be wondering what a neuropsychological or psychological evaluation entails. You can consult with a mental health professional for you to determine which evaluation is best for your child's needs. At our office, the evaluation is three steps: the first session is the clinical interview (generally about 60 minutes to gather background information, complete paperwork, and discuss the evaluation), the next session is the actual psychological testing (depending on the testing needed and age of the child, the testing process can take anywhere from 3-6 hours, not including the report writing and scoring time), and the final session is the feedback session (which generally takes another 60 minutes) to review the results and go over the treatment planning.

How to prepare for the clinical interview (first consultation)

It is completely normal to have some anxiety at the first session, as many parents often do. After all, you may never have been to a psychologist's office before and you may not know what to expect. First, give yourself a pat on the back for taking a step into attending an appointment that most people find very scary and intimidating. I know many psychologists, though, that can ease that tension and worry in the first session; so, hopefully, you will quickly be brought to ease. For the clinical interview, you will be asked a comprehensive set of questions about the medical and psychiatric history of your child, as well as your child's overall well-being. The initial clinical interview is an opportunity for your psychologist to learn more about the occurrences of your child's behavior, what has or has not been done in the past to intervene, as well as their overall functioning.

Some of the areas that are generally assessed during a clinical interview include the following areas, and here is a sample of the types of questions you may be asked:

Reason for visit

What brought you in for the visit? What are the major concerns? For how long has the problem been occurring? What do the symptoms look like in your child? How frequent is the problem? How intense is the reaction to the stressors your child may be experiencing?

School
Learning difficulties? Relationship with peers? Relationships with teachers? Grades? Behavior?

Employment (for older teens)
Functioning on the job? Relationship with supervisors? Relationship with coworkers?

Family
Who lives in the household? What is the dynamic of the household? How would you describe your relationship with your child? Their relationships with siblings? Relationships among family members? Is extended family important? What is discipline like in your family?

Spirituality
Religious beliefs? If so, how important to family?

Culture
Any specific beliefs or customs your family engages in that are important for the evaluation?

Mental health
Any previous psychological evaluations? Is there a history of counseling? History of medication for psychiatric purposes? What were the results of the evaluations or counseling services? Any history of your child trying to engage in self-harming behaviors or harming others? Any hospitalizations for mental health purposes? History of hallucinations or delusions?

Peers

Has your child been bullied in the past? Do they easily make friends? How do they do in groups? Have they been aggressive towards others – if so, in what ways?

Leisure

What does your child like to do for fun? Do they primarily like solo activities or activities with others?

Abuse

Has there been any history of child abuse or neglect?

Substances

Has your child engaged in any substance use that you are aware of? Any previous programs for substances?

Pregnancy history of the mother

Was the child delivered on time? Late? Early? Any complications during the delivery or pregnancy? How much did your child weigh at birth?

Infancy years

Breastfed or formula in infancy? Any allergies in infancy? Any significant issues with eating or sleeping? What was their personality and temperament like?

Developmental milestones

Walking, talking, toilet training, and other milestones – were they on time? Early? Late? Any concerns in any of the areas?

Family history
Any family history of any mental health or physical health conditions? If so, whom?

Medical history
When was your child's last physical? Any recent bloodwork? If so, what were the results? Any history of medical injuries, illness, hospitalizations, surgeries? What medications, if any, are they currently taking? Any loss of consciousness or history of seizures?

> *It is completely normal to have some anxiety at the first session...*

Although psychologists are not medical doctors, what they do is they take the time to assess medically how your child is doing. And, in some cases, they may, based on what they learn from that interview, start to refer you to different specialists. Perhaps your child needs to see a gastroenterologist if they have stomach issues. Or, maybe there are some unaddressed heart issues and your child needs to see a cardiologist. Maybe, if there are seizures or brain issues it could be a neurologist. Or, it could be a referral to the child's pediatrician.

Overall, the clinical interview allows you to provide a thorough history of your child's issues as well as get your questions answered about the psychological evaluation process. You will have an opportunity to relay various examples of your child's behavior to the psychologist, and it will also allow you the ability to better understand your child and the psychologist will know how to proceed with the appropriate psychological tests that are best suited to answer the questions you may have.

The Psychological Evaluation

There are many parts of a psychological evaluation, including, but not limited to:

LEARNING
Intellectual (IQ)

Generally, an Intelligence Quotient (IQ) test is administered to gather an awareness of the child's intellectual potential. It is important for a psychologist to assess how a child is learning; and, depending on the test, as a parent, you can get information, such as your child's potential to learn verbally, non-verbally, the speed it takes them to complete tasks, attention and concentration abilities, reasoning skills, and other valuable information. The IQ test is compared to other children their chronological age, to obtain a standardized score.

Achievement

Often, an achievement test is given to assess at what age and grade level your child is performing compared to other children their age. This assessment will allow you to see if, via this type of standardized test, your child is achieving where they should be for their age and/or grade. In my experience, there have been numerous children that I have tested that have been substantially below their age/grade levels due to a variety of factors, and sometimes ADHD is a cause for this gap in learning. The good news is that there are many interventions for children who are below their age or grade level. (More information on this can be found in Chapter 5).

School functioning
Something that should be considered is your child's current performance in school. How are their grades? Are they struggling with one particular subject? Or, are they having problems in multiple areas of school? How are they doing on classwork? It will be helpful for you to bring a copy of your child's recent report card to your evaluation for the assessor to gain a sense of how your child is currently performing academically. Any previous school evaluations can also help get additional background information, as well.

Type of learner
What type of learner is your child? Do they learn best visually? Verbally? Hands-on learning? Do you already know whether they need multiple breaks to complete tasks? You may have had conversations with your teacher informally about how your child is learning best. This type of information would be great to bring to your evaluation.

Homework
Homework is often a struggle for children with ADHD. The reality is that sometimes it's just too much! It's unfair to demand a homework

assignment that takes a particular child 2 hours to complete, when the average child is getting it done in 20 minutes. Thankfully, there are modifications available to help your child get through (which we will talk about in Chapter 6).

SOCIAL

Peers

Be prepared to discuss how your child is relating to peers, whether it is same-aged peers or younger peers, as well as older peers. It is really important for the psychologist to understand how your child is relating to others, because some children with ADHD do struggle socially, while others do not. Is your child struggling to make friends? Perhaps they are struggling to keep friends once they make friends? Are they having difficulties with self-control and becoming too hyperactive or impulsive around other children? How does your child work within a group of their peers? Do they shy away from a group project, or are they eager to work with others? All of these questions can be helpful for you to begin to think about. If you have not had a psychological evaluation as of yet, you may wish to jot down some notes in this category and other categories to bring to your appointment. There will also be tests to examine your child's social functioning.

Adults

Many children I have met are wonderful with adults, but they have a difficult time with their peers. There is no "right or wrong" with your child's comfort level when it comes to their social development, but it is something to observe and report during the evaluation. You may notice that your child does well with his/her teacher and adults in the family, but not with unfamiliar adults. Familiarity is something that is comforting to many children during social development. Overall, discuss any concerns you have regarding your child's discomfort level interacting with peers and adults.

Bullying
Is your child a victim of bullying? Has your child engaged in bullying behavior? Or, is there a combination? Getting these questions answered are also important because it allows for the psychologist to start to assess for social difficulties and any traumatic incidents. Unfortunately, I have met way too many children that have been victims of bullying. Many children are afraid to speak up about bullying, but they may be open to speaking confidentially in a mental health provider's office. According to stopbullying.gov, "28% of US students in grades 6-12 experience bullying".[8] When you think of the millions of students in the US, that statistic is rather alarming! In some circumstances, the bullying is so chronic or severe that the bullying is truly the

...if you only treat ADHD without treating all conditions, you are not fully helping your child.

source of the behavioral issues or attention problems, which is why this is an important conversation for you to have with your mental health professional.

Often, children affected by bullying can exhibit signs of inattention (as they are thinking about a prior bullying incident or the next time that they could be bullied), hyperactivity (due to nervousness regarding the person who may be hurting them verbally or physically), behavioral issues (due to "acting out" in response to having a difficult time coping with others ridiculing them or physically attacking them). Bullying victims can be mistakenly observed as having ADHD, when they actually may be hiding that someone is engaging in bullying practices towards them. "Only about 20 to 30% of students who are bullied notify adults about the bullying," according to stopbullying.gov.[9]

Alternatively, although it is difficult for any parent to think about, your child may be bullying others. It is hard to think of your child as someone who is bullying others, but it is important to recognize that this behavior may be related to your child struggling with being a victim of bullying themselves, or they may have some social skills difficulties in how to best relate to others.

EMOTIONS
Managing strong emotions
Another part of the evaluation should assess how your child manages their emotions. Does your child cope well with emotion-laden situations?

How do they handle anger? Frustration? Sadness? Nervousness? Some children with ADHD also struggle to manage their emotions due to self-control issues or problems with impulsivity. Many children have problems with "thinking before they act," but not all children. Overall, though, it's important to have a discussion about how your child deals with their emotions. What comments have their teachers made regarding their ability to handle challenging tasks in school? How do they cope with frustrations at home? Do they think before they act, or are their actions more impulsive in nature? Are they overly talkative?

It is also helpful to speak about what triggers your child's emotional reactions, if known. For some children, they are "triggered" by the word "no". It is difficult for them to respond to hearing "no" to something that they want. They may display difficulties managing their frustration or anger when hearing "no." For other children, they become very distracted and triggered by other students talking around them, the air conditioner sound, and other distractions around them. Your child may become distracted and start to talk to others, stray off task with their schoolwork, or get into trouble for "horseplay" behavior. Still other children are "daydreamers" and do not display hyperactivity or impulsivity, but instead they daydream and are inattentive and stray off task often.

Emotional conditions
There are times when ADHD is confused with a child having emotional difficulties, such as

depression, anxiety, a behavioral issue, or another emotional condition. Comprehensive psychological evaluations are important because they are not "just" looking at ADHD, but rather other factors that can mimic ADHD, such as an emotional condition. You may not realize it, but your child may be sad, nervous, or coping with a major change in the family or their school. Therefore, your psychologist will likely evaluate your child to rule out whether depression, anxiety, Obsessive-Compulsive Disorder, Oppositional Defiant Disorder, or another emotional factor may be contributing.

The body of research shows that various conditions are often associated with ADHD diagnoses. So, it's important to remember that other conditions may look like ADHD, but also sometimes children have ADHD along with other conditions. Most importantly, always remember that if you only treat ADHD without treating all conditions, you are not fully helping your child. Remember to get a comprehensive look at all the factors present, so you can get the best treatment options available to treat their symptoms.

BEHAVIOR
Another component of the psychological evaluation is to get into more details about your child's behavior. What is the frequency of their negative behavior? Are they having difficulties mostly at home? Mostly at school? Or both? Frequency is important so that the psychologist can put into perspective the nature of the behavioral occurrences

in order to develop the best recommendations, along with the test data from the report.

Another issue is to examine the duration of the behavior. How long have you observed your child experiencing attention and concentration problems? I have often heard from parents that they wait several years to obtain help, thinking the child will "grow out of it", or they may say, "I thought it was a phase." Either way, it is important to share with your psychologist how long the suspected ADHD and other symptoms have been occurring.

Thirdly, how intense is the behavior? If your child is having behavioral outbursts, for instance, how long might the tantrum be occurring? Is the tantrum lasting for 10 minutes? 1 hour? Several hours? The intensity of the child's behavior is very important in the assessment process to fully evaluate the implications for your child's behavior.

Lastly, has your child had referrals or suspensions from school? Any trouble with the law? Again, looking at the nature of their behavior is very important when evaluating for ADHD and other mental health conditions. Additionally, should your child exhibit symptoms of hyperactivity and/ or impulsivity, you will want to provide detailed examples of these incidents at home and/or at school to help your examiner understand your child best.

FAMILY DYNAMICS
Your psychologist will also complete a clinical interview, and one of the many components will be

to evaluate your current family dynamics. Have there been any recent changes in the family? Any recent moves? The loss of a family member? Separation or divorce of a parent? New sibling? It's important to understand that sometimes children's behaviors, such as problems concentrating on school work, increased hyperactivity, or behavioral issues are linked to them not being able to process a recent change in the family as opposed to ADHD. This is why it is so important to get a thorough evaluation. Again, one of the reasons that ADHD is over-diagnosed is that nuances such as assessing family dynamics are missed, and a child can be diagnosed with ADHD, when they are really struggling to express their feelings about a family incident.

For instance, take an 8-year-old boy who is dealing with the divorce of his parents. He is afraid to talk to either parent because he does not want to "choose sides". He begins to "look" hyperactive in class because he is actually anxious about what is going on at home. His grades start to decline because he cannot concentrate on his schoolwork. When the teacher calls on him, he is often staring off into space, thinking about his parents arguing and his new situation with two houses and two different sets of rules. The teacher gets upset because he is "just not focusing" and he begins to feel frustrated. With this frustration, he now refuses to do his schoolwork, leading to a referral at school. He's also having problems at home, because he now does not want to do chores or his homework. As you can see from this example, this little boy's world could come spiraling downward and he could easily be labeled with "ADHD", but the reality is he is having difficulties coping with a pending divorce.

TRAUMA

Sometimes a child's trauma may be forgotten about when thinking about the impact on a child. A recent loss in the family, abuse, multiple moves, natural disasters, loss of a job of a family member, and other factors may affect your child more than they are willing to admit or want to talk about at that time. It's so important in the evaluation process for you to talk about any traumas that you are aware of, but also know that there may be a situation where a child has internalized an event that did not seem "traumatic" to you as an adult, but may have been very frightening to the child. Just as in the behavioral section, there are reactions that children may have to trauma that "look like" ADHD, but are traumatic reactions. Many children and teens are diagnosed with ADHD when their reactions to their environment are actually due to trauma. Additionally, some children have ADHD, but also need to work through some incidents of trauma.

Interestingly enough, it's important to realize that what we do not think of as traumatic to us as adults, may very well have been traumatic for a young child. I have met children who have told me stories of trauma through bullying and cyberbullying, and this trauma contributes to their current symptoms of inattention, behavioral problems, and/or hyperactivity. Teens have also been "traumatized" by prior relationships. Although, to adults it may only be "puppy love" or a breakup, to a teen, it could very well be a very difficult trauma or stressor in their life, and they could have difficulties adjusting. For that reason, it is important to discuss incidents of major stressors during the evaluation process.

It is also normal if you are not aware of what the major stressor in your child and teen's life might be. Many parents are shocked to learn from a child during a session that the death of a loved one many years ago or a natural disaster many years ago was still affecting them. Youth are sometimes afraid to share their stresses with their parents because they do not want to be a "burden" to their parents or they do not feel they have an outlet to share their feelings. Either way, once you learn of this information, providing this information during the evaluation process will provide more details for your psychologist to understand your child's history and needs. The Atlantic published an article that discussed how it was found that many children were misdiagnosed with ADHD due to trauma.[10]

Chapter 5

Special Education Services

Chances are, if your child has ADHD, they may qualify for accommodations (also known as modifications) in their academic environment. While a diagnosis of ADHD does not automatically mean that your child will need or be given assistance in school, ADHD may be a disability eligible for consideration. Each child with a disability is entitled to Free Appropriate Public Education (FAPE) under the requirements of Section 504 of The Rehabilitation Act of 1973. The US Department of Education provides a document that can be helpful for you.[11]

What is a 504 plan?

A 504 plan is a document that schools use to provide modifications to help your child. The website www2.ed.gov has an excellent document which explains Section 504 more in depth.[12] See an excerpt here:

Section 504 of the Rehabilitation Act[vi]

Section 504 prohibits discrimination on the basis of disability in programs or activities receiving Federal financial assistance, including school districts.[vii] (In this document, "school district" and "public elementary and secondary school systems" are used synonymously and include all local educational agencies (LEAs) and charter schools.) [viii]

The definition of disability is the same under both Title II and Section 504. Under these laws, a person (including a student) with a disability is one who meets any of the following criteria:

— has a physical or mental impairment that substantially limits one or more major life activities;

— has a record of such an impairment; or

— is regarded as having such an impairment.[ix]

Some examples of a major life activity that could be substantially limited by ADHD include concentrating, reading, thinking, and functions of the brain.[x]

[vi] For further discussion of these laws, please visit OCR's website, at http://www.ed.gov/policy/rights/guid/ocr/disability.html.

[vii] Title II prohibits discrimination on the basis of disability by public entities, including

public elementary and secondary school systems, regardless of receipt of Federal financial assistance. In the education context, OCR shares enforcement responsibility for Title II with the U.S. Department of Justice. 28 C.F.R. § 35.190(b)(2). Although this document primarily addresses Section 504 obligations, violations of Section 504 that result from a school district's failure to meet the obligations identified in this letter also constitute violations of Title II. 42 U.S.C. § 12201(a). To the

> *Be an advocate for your child, but also approach the meeting with a positive attitude.*

extent that Title II provides greater protection than Section 504, covered entities must comply with Title II's requirements, see, e.g., *Guidance on Effective Communication for Students with Hearing, Vision, or Speech Disabilities in Public Elementary and Secondary Schools* (Nov. 12, 2014), http://www.ed.gov/about/offices/list/ocr/letters/colleague-effective-communication-201411.pdf. A discussion of any such additional requirements is beyond the scope of this guidance.

The requirements of Section 504 regarding the provision of FAPE also apply to any juvenile justice facility that receives federal financial assistance from the Department of Education, and the requirements of Title II apply to any juvenile justice facility that is a program or activity of a state or local government. *See* OCR and Department of Justice Civil Rights Division, *Dear Colleague Letter: Civil Rights in Juvenile Justice Residential Facilities* (Dec. 8, 2014), http://www.ed.gov/policy/gen/guid/correctional-education/cr-letter.pdf. For more information on Title II, please visit https://www.ada.gov/.

viii Charter schools are subject to the same Federal civil rights obligations as all other public schools. "Charter schools" includes schools that are public schools of a school district as well as charter schools that operate as LEAs under State law. For additional information about the applicability of Federal civil rights laws to charter schools, see OCR, *Dear Colleague Letter: Charter Schools* (May 14, 2014), http://www.ed.gov/ocr/letters/colleague-201405-charter.pdf.

ix 29 U.S.C. § 705(20)(B); 34 C.F.R. § 104.3(j). Those who are eligible for coverage under the "regarded as" prong of the disability definition are not entitled to FAPE under Section 504 (because they do not actually have a substantially limiting impairment), *cf.* 42 U.S.C. § 12201(h), but they are still protected by Section 504's general nondiscrimination provisions, including protection from disability-based harassment, and retaliation.

x 42 U.S.C. § 12102.

Examples of accommodations may include:

- sitting closer to the teacher (to reduce distractions),

- extended time on tests, quizzes, and/ or standardized testing (as attention and concentration issues can often times affect performance speed),

- less homework (given in some cases where homework is too frustrating and the workload needs to be decreased, but learning is still accomplished),

- use of fidget toys (if a child is needing to often "do" something with their hands), and

- various ways to organize information (depending on the age of the child, these demands vary with elementary, middle and high school levels).

You may already have a 504 plan in place, but you may need to update the plan to include or exclude modifications. In either case, here are some tips for attending a 504 plan meeting:

1. Attend! This may sound strange, but many parents struggle to attend meetings, saying work or another function would interfere with this meeting. It is extremely important to attend these meetings so you can be well-informed about what is going on in your child's educational life. Take the time off from work to attend and work with the school to find a time that best suits you, but you'll need to recognize school hours as well.

2. Be an informant. Let the school know what you are seeing at home as problems. For example,

the team won't know the details of your child's homework struggles unless you let them know.

3. Carry a folder with any recent psychological evaluations, physician recommendations, or any other important health care documents.

4. Determine ahead of time what your child's primary needs are at this meeting.

5. Explain the reasons why you think your child may need some new accommodations on their 504 plan. You may have documentation from teacher notes that you wish to bring in and discuss.

6. Focus! Don't forget to stay focused and ask lots of questions to clarify the 504 plan process.

7. Gather copies of new documents at the meeting to add to your child's educational file. It will be a great idea to bring this 504 plan to your follow-up appointments with mental health providers.

8. Have faith. Be an advocate for your child, but also approach the meeting with a positive attitude. Bring a fresh, positive energy into a meeting where the results may potentially change your child's educational experience.

Additude Mag has a great resource with links on how to write letters to schools, requesting accommodations.[13]

What is an Individual Education Plan (IEP)?

An Individual Education Plan (IEP) is another document that provides modifications for a child's learning environment, but the disabilities are different under the IEP.[14] A child with ADHD and other conditions, like a learning disability or speech therapy needs, or Gifted needs, etc. may need an IEP because this document requires a change in the curriculum of the student. Sometimes accommodations are also provided under the "OHI" (Other Health Impaired) section of the IEP as well for students with ADHD. The Department of Education provides "A Guide to the Individualized Education Program", and an excerpt is provided here regarding what an IEP contains:[15]

By law, the IEP must include certain information about the child and the educational program designed to meet his or her unique needs. In a nutshell, this information is:

- **Current performance.** The IEP must state how the child is currently doing in school (known as present levels of educational performance). This information usually comes from the evaluation results such as classroom tests and assignments, individual tests given to decide eligibility for services or during reevaluation, and observations made by parents, teachers, related service providers, and other school staff. The statement about "current performance" includes how the child's disability affects his or her involvement and progress in the general curriculum.

- **Annual goals.** These are goals that the child can reasonably accomplish in a year. The goals are broken down into short-term objectives or benchmarks. Goals may be academic, address social or behavioral needs, relate to physical needs, or address other educational needs. These goals must be measurable – meaning that it must be possible to measure whether the student has achieved these goals.

- **Special education and related services.** The IEP must list the special education and related services to be provided to the child or on behalf of the child. This includes supplementary aids and services that the child needs. It also includes modifications (changes) to the program or supports for school personnel – such as training or professional development – that will be provided to assist the child.

- **Participation with nondisabled children.** The IEP must explain the extent (if any) to which the child will not participate with non-disabled children in the regular class and other school activities.

- **Participation in state and district-wide tests.** Most states and districts give achievement tests to children in certain grades or age groups. The IEP must state what modifications in the administration of these tests the child will need. If a test is not appropriate for the child, the IEP must state why the test is not appropriate and how the child will be tested instead.

- **Dates and places.** The IEP must state when services will begin, how often they will be provided, where they will be provided, and how long they will last.

- **Transition service needs.** Beginning when the child is age 14 (or younger, if appropriate), the IEP must address (within the applicable parts of the IEP) the courses he or she needs to take to reach his or her post-school goals. A statement of transition services needs must also be included in each of the child's subsequent IEPs.

- **Needed transition services.** Beginning when the child is age 16 (or younger, if appropriate), the IEP must state what transition services are needed to help the child prepare for leaving school.

- **Age of majority.** Beginning at least one year before the child reaches the age of majority, the IEP must include a statement that the student has been told of any rights that will transfer to him or her at the age of majority. (This statement would be needed only in states that transfer rights at the age of majority.)

- **Measuring progress.** The IEP must state how the child's progress will be measured and how parents will be informed of that progress.

Different states may vary in their formatting of an IEP, so it is important to follow up with the school should your child need an IEP to assess how you can best support your child during the IEP process and what information would be most helpful for you to contribute to the process. Make sure to ask as many questions as you need at the meetings so you are clear on the expectations for your child. Also, you will want to talk to your child at an age-appropriate level about the school's expectations and some of the changes that may be occurring in their classroom. The goal is to appropriately prepare them for new structural modifications and express how these changes are designed to benefit them and allow them an opportunity to be more successful in their school settings. The more preparation they have, the better chances of them having fewer adjustment issues to new and surprising changes.

The reality is this: school cannot be the same for everyone.

You will want to discuss with your psychologist and school academic team which accommodations are right for your situation, whether the IEP or 504 plan. There are many resources for IEPs, and the Department of Education has a sample IEP on their website so you can become familiar with the format. You can also ask your school district to give you a sample blank copy of the template so you can understand what goes into either document.

Understood.org has a great checklist: "What to Bring to an IEP meeting" that can be beneficial to you in your meeting.[16]

Sample accommodations for a child with ADHD:

Organization

- Have the teacher write assignments in a notebook for your child. If your child struggles to remember to write down homework or classwork tasks, the teacher may provide a copy of the assignment, as opposed to your child writing down the information incorrectly or forgetting to write it down.

- Create a system for ensuring that homework is taken out of your child's backpack at school. I've heard numerous stories of well-meaning parents and children that work so hard on homework, yet homework is forgotten in the backpack all day and does not make it into the homework bin at school.

- A teacher can color code information handed to the student, so they can understand what is most important.

Inattentiveness

- A peer may be assigned to help your child with note-taking; or, in some cases, the teacher may make copies of notes and give them to your child.

- For older children, they may be permitted to use a digital recorder to take notes, to refer back to information they may have missed during the class.

- Frequent breaks can be beneficial to help in the learning process and reduce frustration from inattentiveness

- Reducing distractions is important, and one way can be through creating a quiet zone at the school for your child to take tests and quizzes.

- Repeating instructions and reminders of expectations can be helpful to refocus your child.

- A seating arrangement where your child sits closer to the front of the classroom can help to avoid distractions from others.

- A nonverbal signal to get your child "back on track" if they are daydreaming can work to refocus your child; such as, a certain "look" from the teacher or another signal that only the teacher and child know about. Having a nonverbal signal is sometimes helpful so that the teacher does not have to verbally single out your child.

Hyperactivity/Impulsivity
- Use of therapeutic fidget items can help with "busy hands". Ideally, the item should be a

quiet item that does not disturb others, but an item that can help to refocus some increased energy. Therapy Shoppe is one example of an online store that specializes in special needs items, such as fidget toys.[17]

- If working at a desk is difficult, the use of a computer can also be helpful with some tasks.

- Allowing the child to get up from their seat and take a physical break can also help.

- If there is a behavioral issue, a specific behavioral plan may be helpful in school where a special reward system is established to promote positive behavior.

- For older children, they may be permitted to leave the class a little early to get to the next class, should they be getting too distracted in the hallways.

Tests, quizzes, and assignments
- Extended time for class demands can work to decrease the frustration sometimes associated with getting off task and not having enough time to finish an assignment.

- Having directions read aloud can be an accommodation, especially with standardized testing, to be sure your child is on track with their task.

- A separate room to take important tests and quizzes may be helpful to reduce distractions

- Reduced homework can also be beneficial
  to reduce unnecessary frustration with
  assignments that are simply too long for
  your child to complete. An example would be,
  instead of doing all 30 math problems, that
  they do only the odd numbers. There is no
  need for your child to spend unnecessary time
  on tasks which lead to agitation.

The value of accommodations

Many parents have asked if accommodations
are a "crutch" for their child and if they should really
use them. The reality is this: school cannot be the
same for everyone. To think that every classroom
would have different students fulfilled by the same
teaching methods would be flawed. Children learn
differently, and children have disabilities and
needs that should be attended to. Consider this:
not everyone will have the same job in life! Some
people do well with fast-paced jobs, others are more
slow-paced, and that is perfectly okay. The same
holds true for school. Your child may need to use the
accommodations temporarily in elementary school,
but some children need to use them until their teen
years. Some teens continue to have modification
into their adult and employment years. Overall, it
is really about making sure that your child has a fair
playing field in their educational experience.

Another issue to consider is whether or not
your child might benefit from counseling services
provided at the school. Not all schools have this

capability, but you could certainly ask as to whether counseling services are an option, as a service from their IEP. Individual therapy may be helpful if your child is struggling with ADHD symptoms and it is especially noticeable in their academic performance. The school may work with you to set up individual therapy times (which may be once a week, for instance), to work on ways to reduce your child's inattention issues, impulsivity, hyperactivity, or other symptoms interfering with their school life. Sometimes, a school may also offer a social skills group where children with ADHD can practice how to interact appropriately with other same-aged peers. A group can also be useful to build your child's self-esteem by introducing them to peers that may be experiencing the same struggles they are. I have often heard children talk about how they feel alone with a diagnosis of ADHD. Of course, as adults, we know there are millions of children diagnosed with ADHD and they are truly not alone. But, to a child, it means more to meet another child with the same condition many times to reduce that sense of isolation. There are also counseling options outside of school, which we'll talk about in Chapter 9.

Chapter 6

Communication with the School

It is imperative for you to communicate regularly and efficiently with the school system. There are several ways for you to make the communication process a successful one throughout your child's academic experience. In this chapter, you will learn how to navigate through the school system with a child with ADHD.

Parent-teacher communication

At the beginning of the school year, you may wish to bring information to your child's teacher about their ADHD diagnosis. Sometimes, teachers read the educational file and learn there that your child has ADHD, but it can be more helpful to explain to the teacher that your child has ADHD and what that means for your child. Remember, you know your child best and you can be the best source regarding your child's symptoms. ADHD does not "look" the same in every child, so it's important that your child's teacher know your child's specific symptoms.

Your child may also have another condition, such as depression, anxiety, or a learning disability, which you should also discuss with the teacher. In our practice, we often provide literature that can be given to the teacher to help them understand what ADHD may look like. You can find great examples of literature to give to your child's teacher at the helpguide.org website.[18] This site has excellent handouts that you can print and review with your child's teacher. Remember to also read the information yourself, and highlight sections that best describe your child. You can also add information to the printouts that may not be included in the literature. Overall, the point is to make the information customized to your child, to help the teacher.

Attend parent-teacher conferences regularly. These conferences can be a great resource for getting information about what is going on with your child with respect to their grades, their relationship with their teacher, social skills they are using with their parents, and their overall work ethic and learning styles. There are some teachers who are wonderful with scheduling parent-teacher conferences; but, with other teachers, you may have to initiate more meetings. That's okay! The main point is to remember that it is your responsibility to maintain frequent communication with your child's teacher.

Overall, be open with the process of communication. Just as with everything in life, you will encounter some teachers that will work excellently with your child, follow the suggested accommodations for ADHD, and work well with the personality of your child. But, sometimes, you will encounter teachers that may have stereotypes about ADHD and will not be willing to implement the classroom modifications, and generally "clash" with your child. Either way, keeping the lines of communication open, through the various channels provided by the teacher can be helpful. Many parents have expressed to me that teachers have given them email addresses, phone numbers, and overall have provided a variety of ways for them to stay in contact in efforts to best communicate about their child.

Folder or e-folder with information

Keeping a folder with your child's information organized can be helpful to have when communicating with the school about services for your child. Wrightslaw.com has some suggestions and charts for organizing your child's information.[19] Be sure to include your child's psychological evaluation, medical records (or have easy access to them), 504 plan, IEP documents, recent report card, and any other health or behavior information that may be relevant to working with the school. If you have a recent psychological evaluation, for instance, which added more information that was not previously included in the educational plan, be sure to provide this data to the school in a timely manner. This knowledge may be necessary to modify the 504 plan or IEP that may better help your child's academic outcomes.

You may also wish to have an e-folder, where you scan documents and keep a virtual file of information, including recent report cards, important teacher comments, and other evaluation reports. An e-folder can help to reduce clutter and you can print the paper file, when needed.

What should you do if the school is not cooperating?

Unfortunately, sometimes the school system may not cooperate with you in your requests to help your child with their disability. There are steps that you may wish to take, should you not find your child is best helped by their teacher. You could request a meeting with the assistant principal or principal to further discuss your concerns. Should you not receive a satisfactory response from your child's principal, you may wish to discuss your concerns with your district's coordinator for Exceptional Student Education (ESE) programs. It would help to explain your child's needs, what the school has done to help, and what else could be helpful for your child to be most successful in their academic environment. In more intense cases, you may need to consult with the school board to get a resolution of your concerns for your child. Either way, know that you have the right to advocate for the best interests of your child.

In some cases, you may wish to use an IEP advocate. If you search online for an IEP advocate in your area, you may find someone that can help guide you through the process of an IEP meeting and discuss with the IEP the needs of your child. An IEP advocate can also help to attend meetings in some cases or serve as consultants before, after, or during the meeting. Additionally, Additude Mag discusses how to obtain an educational advocate.[20]

Attend parent-teacher conferences regularly.

A special education attorney may also help to answer legal questions about the process of obtaining or modifying an IEP or receiving special education services. Some parents have found it helpful to discuss legal questions and what the rights of their child are before the meeting. Regardless of which consultant you use, stay informed, and document your child's experience with receiving services for their ADHD symptoms. Your child deserves to receive the appropriate accommodations to help them be successful in their endeavors!

If you believe that your child has been discriminated against on the basis of their disability, you should be aware that, in some cases, parents have been recommended to contact the

Office for Civil Rights (OCR) under the Department of Education. According to a "Dear Colleague" letter from the Assistant Secretary for Civil Rights (7/26/2016), this excerpt expresses the cases of ADHD complaints:[21]

> "Over the past five fiscal years (2011-2015), the Department's Office for Civil Rights (OCR) has received more than 16,000 complaints alleging discrimination on the basis of disability in elementary and secondary education programs. Approximately 2,000, or one in nine, of these complaints involved allegations of discrimination against a student with ADHD. In resolving such complaints, OCR has found that many teachers and administrators often take appropriate action to ensure that students with ADHD receive the protections to which they are entitled under Federal law, but many others are not familiar with this disorder, or how it could impact a student's equal access to a school district's program."

Therefore, it is imperative to communicate frequently for your child's benefit, to advocate for their needs, and to educate faculty and staff about your child, as necessary.

Homeschool or Virtual School?

Communication with the district is important if your child is enrolled in a home school or virtual program as well. Documentation of your child's ADHD is still very much important. Depending on the structure of the academic program, you may not necessarily have much communication with another "teacher", but you will have to interact with the coordinator of the district or school program. It is still critical to remain an advocate for your child with ADHD. You may wish to attend a homeschool conference, and the Great Homeschool Conventions website has examples of various conferences across the country.[22] At a conference, you may receive additional support from other parents of children with ADHD in a homeschool program. They have great resources to help support you in the process of homeschooling a child with ADHD. Should you have instructors that you do communicate with as a parent, be sure to email them information about how your child learns best and any limitations your child may have with completing assignments, due to their ADHD condition.

Have a team approach

Just as how you have a team approach outside of the school, which may consist of a mental health professional, family physician, neurologist, and other providers (speech-language therapist, occupational therapist, etc.), you should also have a plan to have a team inside of the school to best help your child. Often, there is an ESE team, but the composition of this team will likely vary from school to school. At some schools, the ESE team may consist of a teacher, an ESE specialist, a school psychologist or another mental health professional, and another staff member. It is important to learn who represents your child's academic team and what you can do to work with this team. Collaboration is key. If materials are requested from the academic team, submit them in a timely manner. Should you need to reach out to the team, learn the culture of the school and how you can best communicate in the most effective manner. Also, be clear on the time frames for communication. Some teams will say what the timeframe would be for you to expect a response on the process.

> *...having a "team approach" is about more than just knowing who the members of the team are. It's also a mindset.*

But, having a "team approach" is about more than just knowing who the members of the team are. It's also a mindset. I have seen too many parents and teachers play the "blame" game and want to say that the other party is responsible for the child's well-being. The reality is, we are all responsible for a child's outcome, in both the home and school settings. It's about doing your best to work with the school environment. In some intense circumstances, might you need to request a change of teacher or change of school? Of course, but first do your best to work with the school environment and keep the educational experience as stable as possible for your child. It would not be helpful to move your child multiple times from school to school; instead, it is most beneficial to request the appropriate environmental changes for your child and advocate for their needs. Many children need structure and stability in their school experiences, so changing schools should not be the first option.

Chapter 7

How to Help
Your Child
in the Classroom

Homework

You may find that your child has been struggling with homework because they have a hard time concentrating for long periods or they have a difficult time blocking out distractions. Either way, it is important to approach your child's teacher if homework is becoming a major issue. Your goal should be to reduce the amount of homework to a level where your child is still learning, but they are not so frustrated that they feel like giving up altogether.

If you have found that you cannot successfully work on homework assignments together with your child, perhaps because it's too much for you to handle as well, consider hiring a tutor. Many tutors can work one on one with your child (or in a small group setting) and still accomplish your learning goals. We all know that some children will have conflicts completing homework with a parent at home, regardless of how great their parent is doing to teach those concepts, so why not make it easier and hire a tutor if it will lead to fewer struggles in the family?

Remember, your overall goal is that you want your child to be happy, healthy, and productive in life, and many of the smaller arguments will not matter as much.

There are a variety of tutoring options. Many schools have free tutoring services after school, so check with your child's school for options. Sometimes libraries can also be a great place to find tutoring. A tutor who is an older student, maybe a high school or college student, can also work great to meet your needs. Virtual tutors are also becoming more popular. If you take a look at the Huntington website, they are an example of tutors who focus on tutoring children with ADHD and their site illustrates their customized approach.[23] Whichever method you choose, find a tutor that works best for you and your child's unique learning strengths.

Similar to how you have informed your child's teacher of their ADHD diagnosis, you should also discuss your child's ADHD needs with their tutor. Explain what your child's main distractors are and positive ways you have found to work with them at home. You may have the case where your tutor works in special education or is a teacher who is familiar with children with ADHD. You may also have a tutor who is an 11th grade student and not really aware of how to work best with a child with ADHD. Again, it is your responsibility to explain what your child needs and have suggestions for how the tutor can help your child.

Something that is really important to think about at home is how is your child's homework space organized. Especially for the younger child, make sure that their space has everything they need. Do you have their pencils, paper, books, assignments, snack, water, tissue all in one place? Having everything organized helps prevent getting up often from their seat to look for items. Remember, the goal is completion of their work, so your child may want to be in a quiet place, or they may prefer to be in the middle of the "action" in the house, say the kitchen table, where there are other activities happening around them. While these are suggestions in this chapter, remember to do what works best for your child. I can't emphasize that enough... do what works best! Pick your battles. Remember, your overall goal is that you want your child to be happy, healthy, and productive in life, and many of the smaller arguments will not matter as much.

School Relationships

Relationships at school should be nurtured. Building healthy, positive relationships can help the social-emotional development of your child. But, what if your child is struggling in school with making friends? Talk to your child about their daily experiences with their friends, which is important no matter how old they are. Your child in their younger years may love to talk about their experiences playing with their classmates; but, as they get older, you may have to encourage more conversation about their daily school life. You may wish to see how your child can get involved in school activities, such as clubs and extracurricular activities, as part of your efforts for them to be more socialized in school. Find activities that they are good at and enjoy. If your child hates sports, but loves music or art, remember to find those activities they enjoy and where they are willing to socially interact with others. If your child gets invited to a birthday party, make efforts to take them, so they can practice interacting with others. Still, when you receive comments from your child's teacher about your child's social relationships, be sure to follow up with your child. Take the time to review their social experience and roleplay at home what they should and should not do in social situations.

There are many children with ADHD that I have worked with, where they recognize a social deficit, but they have said, "I don't know what to say" or, "I don't know what to do." The child has a deep desire to connect with their peers, but they struggle due to hyperactivity and impulsivity.

If that is the case for your child, work with your child on example situations:

- "If another child says to you, 'You're stupid', what do you say?"

- "If your friend makes fun of you because you go to a smaller group for reading, what do you say?"

- "If someone in your class says, 'You're ugly", what should you do?"

Although these questions may seem basic to you as an adult, remember that, for an 8-year-old child, this is their world where children call children names all the time; especially, "stupid" "ugly" or some other demeaning comments. Sometimes, even elementary schoolers observe that your child may have a therapeutic fidget item they are using, and they may be made fun of because of their disability. Teach your child how to respond to others making fun of them because of their differences. Remind them of all the strengths they have and how wonderful they are, and your child needs to remember that their disability does NOT define them.

Your child's relationship with their teacher is also equally important. There are wonderful teachers that are very familiar with working effectively with a child with ADHD, and there are teachers that are newer to the field of education and do not have any experience working with children with ADHD. And, of course, there are many teachers in the middle. Encourage a positive relationship between your child and their teacher. Talk to them about their day and their experience with their teacher. If they say, "I hate my teacher", be sure to follow up and get more details. Your child may have difficulties because of a clash of personalities with their teacher or because of a clash of their learning style and how the teacher approaches the classroom. It's important to remind your child that it is unlikely that they will like every single teacher they have throughout their entire educational career, but they have to respect their teacher.

Establish a behavior plan with your child's teacher.

Another area of importance is bullying. Does your child show signs of being bullied at school? Some signs of bullying include:

- Sadness
- Withdrawal
- Fear of going to school
- Unexplained bruises or ripped clothing
- Change in personality

- Reduced or increased appetite
- Anxiety
- Declining grades
- Spending less time involved in hobbies and activities
- Talking about wanting to hurt themselves or others

Bullying is something that should be taken very seriously. Pacer.org reported on research that has shown that children with a disability are two to three times more likely to be bullied than their peers.[24] This is why it is so important to do frequent check-ins with your child to ensure that they are not being bullied. There are also bullying apps such as "KnowBullying" to help combat bullying.[25] Immediately approach the school if you suspect your child is being bullied, so you can prevent later emotional, mental, and physical harm for your child. Your school should be proactive in having a plan to ensure your child's safety. If necessary, you may wish to include provisions against bullying behaviors in your child's 504 or IEP at school.

Behavioral difficulties

The book *Smart, but Scattered*, discusses how a child can be very bright, but their disorganization of thoughts and impulsivity can lead to behavioral problems. Sometimes, your child may exhibit "shutting down" behavior in school, where they refuse to do their work, due to the level of frustration with the material. Sometimes they may be in "information overload" where the stimuli of the classroom is simply too much. Your child may be struggling with getting out of their seat often, due to difficulties sitting for long periods. Still other times, your child may have issues with self-control, where they cannot keep their arms and feet to themselves. Of course, there are also children with ADHD who do not exhibit behavioral issues.

Regardless of the behavioral issue your child may experience, it is important to communicate with your child's teacher on a behavioral plan so that your child may have the best academic outcomes. Using some of the previously mentioned accommodations in school, communicating with the teacher and reviewing the school rules at home as well, are definitely great starts to getting your child on the right path. With continued support at home, you can help your child to continue to feel supported through their educational endeavors. According to some research, a daily report card system may also be effective for children with ADHD.[26]

Chapter 8

How to Help Your Child at Home

Organization

One of the biggest complaints that I hear from parents frequently is that their child is disorganized. This could refer to an untidy room, a backpack that is in disarray, unfinished projects, chores left halfway done, or a combination of these things. Fortunately, there are many ways that you can organize your home to help your child be more organized and help them to stay on task.

The first item that you need to assess is your family schedule. Is your child over-scheduled? Is there a lack of structure at home? Is there a homework schedule? A bedtime routine? Play time? Children with ADHD do best with a predictable schedule. Additude Mag has a sample routine that you may download for free from their site.[27] It may also help your child to have some visual representation of their schedule at home. You could list reminders of their morning routine and after-school schedule. A calendar for older children that can read is also beneficial, so they can remember what their after-school routine looks like surrounding their extracurricular activities. It's important, though, that your child is not over-scheduled. Some children have an activity every night of the week, and weekends are so jam-packed that they really do not have a lot of down time, which important for them to "recharge" their energy. So, be mindful of the schedule that you create and do your best to stick to it. Will there be times when life happens and you get off your routine? Of course! But, make a commitment to maintain a structure that works best for your child.

The next item you will need to look is whether or not your child does well with visual aids and charts. Does your child need visual reminders in addition to verbal cues? Some children do great with charts that have their daily routine (which may include things like brushing their teeth, washing their face, taking a bath, eating a healthy meal, etc.) that they can check off with a dry-erase marker. Other children do great with simply seeing a chart of their daily routine and being reminded frequently to check their chart. This chart can be customized into whatever area your child may struggle in.

Therapeutic "fidget" items can also be helpful in the home setting as well as the school environment.

If you have found that your child needs something to "fidget" with while they are watching television, doing their homework, or talking about their day, it can be beneficial to obtain this item for them at home. Your child may do great with a stress ball, as well. Experiment with a few items to see what works best for your child. If you have other children at home, help them to understand that your child needs this item to help them focus.

Children with ADHD do best with a predictable schedule.

The topic of chores may seem like a bore for many children, but chores can be particularly problematic for children with ADHD. Why? Because your child may simply not be focusing on the instructions they have been given to complete a chore. It can often be helpful to provide instructions one step at a time. If you say, "Go clean your room, empty the cat litter, and don't forget to put away your clothes" as a 3-step instruction, that may be too much information, and you might find that only one of those items get completed. Many parents then become upset that not all three tasks have been completed, and when you hear, "Oops, I forgot" from your child, you may find yourself getting angry. Then, there is a power struggle that ensues and an argument about not getting the chore completed. Does this sound familiar? I have heard this scenario often. It's important not to blame your child or yourself in this instance. Instead, work on making the necessary changes to make your household more flexible so that your child can be successful. Generally, children want to please their parents, but it can be very frustrating when the expectations are not set appropriately for them. So remember, a step-by-step approach could work best for your child.

It is critical to have one-on-one time with your child.

Discipline

Many parents have also asked for guidance on the appropriate way to discipline a child with ADHD. First, make sure that you have an expectations list or a set of rules, especially for younger children. Don't assume that your child knows all the rules if you have not gone over the rules with them. Next, do they know what your consequences are for not following the rules? Also, have you established realistic expectations for your child? By no means am I suggesting lowering your expectations for your child or treating them as a "victim" of having ADHD; but, what I am saying is to make sure that your rules are realistic for some of their attention and concentration limitations. Many parents have told me that they were treating their child with ADHD the same as their child without ADHD, but they soon realized that there were simply some things that their child with ADHD could not do the same way as their other child. Remember, it's okay for you to have a conceptually different set of expectations for your children who differ in their strengths.

The question often comes up, should I spank my child who has ADHD? My professional opinion is not to spank your child, because there are numerous research studies that show that spanking can be harmful to a child. You may be thinking, well that's my choice as a parent or that your parents spanked you and you came out "okay." It is absolutely your choice as a parent what disciplinary method you choose to use with your child; but, professionally, I have seen many families that choose not to spank and instead use alternative discipline, such as timeouts, revocation of privileges, talking, and other means to discipline a child with ADHD successfully. Research does show, though, that the best way to achieve positive behavior is through positive reinforcement. This means praising the positive behaviors that you wish to see. Behavior charts also work well in many cases for younger children. Freeprintablebehaviorcharts.com is a great resource to find free behavior charts that you can customize for your child, depending on their needs.[28]

Relationships in the family

Something to keep in mind is the quality of the relationships in your family unit. Since finding out that your child has ADHD, ask yourself: has the bond you have with your child been affected? If so, make efforts to re-strengthen the bond with your child. It is critical to have one-on-one time with your child. You may be saying that it's difficult because you have multiple children in the home; but, make a commitment to have some "special time" with your child, even if it's a 15-minute segment a week at home. Find ways to spend time with one another and remind your child how much you care about them. Remind them of their strengths, and most importantly remind them often that ADHD does not define who they are. There are many ways you can work on building their self-esteem through conversations you can have with them in heart-to-heart conversations. In my first book, *The Practical Guide to Raising Emotionally Healthy Children*, I discuss in more detail ways to build self-esteem with your child. As children get older, they will hear a lot of negative information from peers, media, teachers, and other individuals in their life about ADHD. That's one of the reasons why it is so important for you as their parent to have a strong, positive relationship with them.

Sibling relationships

Sibling relationships are also important. You may have a child with ADHD, and another child without ADHD, who are very different and have a difficult time understanding each other's needs. It is critical that you sit with siblings and explain some of the needs of your child with ADHD. Explain that every child is different and that they each have their own set of strengths. Remind them that family is forever and how much they need each other and support each other. Of course, just as many other siblings do, they will not always understand the value of their sibling bond as children; but, as they get older, they have the opportunity to really be a source of support for one another. Remind your children to "fight fair" and explain what it means to be a sibling to someone with ADHD. Help your child that may not have ADHD understand what they are hearing around them too – maybe from their peers, the media, and other sources in their life. Most importantly, make sure that your child is not being bullied in the home setting for their ADHD symptoms, so make sure that the line is clearly drawn on what is acceptable when it comes to any sibling rivalry. Encourage them to find activities that they both enjoy.

Extended family

Your child may have extended family in their life, such as grandparents, aunts, uncles, cousins, or other family members that play a significant role in their life. Have you considered how to best explain to your family members, who may be critics or skeptics of ADHD, about your child's diagnosis? Have you chosen not to discuss this condition with your extended family? Either way, it's important for you to make a decision that is in the best interests of your family. While there are many possibilities, depending on your family situation, you will want to make sure that your child is best supported. Again, be aware of their surrounding family members and the comments that are being made. It is not helpful if there is a family member who constantly has negative things to say about your child, especially in front of them. I have often witnessed families who are doing the best they can, but family members can be negative and say things like, "ADHD doesn't really exist" or, "He's so ADHD", or other comments that can be downright hurtful. In this case, make sure that your child has a great blend of positive people around them to improve their self-esteem. Talk to your extended family about ways in which you wish to be supported in the process of raising your child and be sure to establish appropriate boundaries when necessary.

Chapter 9

Therapy Services

You may have thought about whether your child would benefit from counseling to treat their ADHD symptoms. Chances are, they may very well benefit from a variety of counseling or therapy options. But, how do you know when it's time to turn to therapy? ADHD can be mild, moderate, or severe. I have had the opportunity to witness many children derive great benefit from therapy services to help them manage their ADHD.

How do you know if your child needs counseling?

One biggest thing to consider when thinking about whether your child needs therapy is how your child is functioning. Academically, how are they doing? Are they struggling in school with the schoolwork? Completing homework in a timely manner? Is their frustration level to a level where you feel you can no longer control it? Are their grades starting to decline? Academic functioning is very important. I have seen too many children suffer academically because of ADHD symptoms that were not properly treated. It is amazing to see what can happen when a child learns to better understand their impulsivity, hyperactivity, and attention/concentration problems. When they begin to learn the triggers for their symptoms and what to do about it, it can truly make a world of difference.

Don't wait until everything fails! Listen to your gut. Get your child counseling to help them.

Socially, how is your child functioning? Are they struggling to interact with peers? Do they have problems with self-control? Are they having difficulties making or keeping friends? Are they having problems within groups in school? You may have tried to have conversations at home and the school may have tried interventions that have not worked to help your child function better socially; but, if you are finding that these attempts are not helpful, you may wish to turn to counseling. Don't get me wrong. Don't wait until everything fails! You are doing your child a disservice by waiting too long; but generally, I have found that many parents have a 'gut instinct' that knows when their child is heading down a scary path. Listen to your gut. Get your child counseling to help them.

Another area that comes up with some ADHD children is when the frustration level may be so difficult that they have thoughts of self-harm or engage in self-harming behavior, such as cutting themselves. If you suspect or catch your child hurting themselves, get help immediately! This is a red flag that your child is having other symptoms, along with ADHD, that should be addressed by a mental health professional. Do not wait. Do not think, "This is a phase", or anything that may put your child in harm's way. Could your child be trying to get attention by saying they want to hurt themselves? Sure, some kids do that: but, do you really want to make that call and take that risk? Get to a mental health professional who can do an evaluation to see what types of interventions would be best for your child.

Behaviorally, how is your child doing? Are they getting referrals or suspensions from school? Are they displaying defiant behavior? Are you often getting calls from the teacher? Significant behavior problems can indicate a need for therapy, as well.

Some things for you to consider are:

- How long has the negative behavior been happening?
- Has there been a recent change at home?
- How often is the behavior happening?
- How intense is the behavioral issue?

All of these questions can be put into perspective for you by a mental health professional who can help you to discern whether the behavior is problematic, typical given the ADHD diagnosis, or a larger cause for concern.

When considering whether to seek therapy for your child, another issue to think about is whether you've tried many things at home, but felt like they weren't working. I've talked to many parents who have tried interventions at home or a change of diet or early bedtimes or another home remedy. Unfortunately, they found these things did not work, and a mental health professional was necessary for intervention. It's often the stigma of mental health that prevents many parents from getting their child the help they need. Don't let this be you! Do what you need to do to get your child the help they need. I'll talk about different types of counseling services in this chapter, but do your own research as well and help your child be successful in their goals.

Individual therapy

Should you decide to get therapy for your child to work one-on-one, there are a variety of factors you'll need to consider. Most importantly, find a therapist that your child really connects with and trusts. It does not matter if your therapist has graduated from an Ivy League school, has 20 years of experience and has a pristine office, the fact is that your child needs to feel comfortable with this person. If you have an option of a specialist, choose someone that specializes in the child and teen population, and always ask the therapist if they have experience working with children with ADHD. The American Psychological Association has a great guide that you can check out to learn more.[29]

For younger children, play therapy can be beneficial, because play is how young children can best communicate and learn therapeutic skills (you can visit the Association for Play Therapy's website for more information).[30] I did play therapy with younger children with ADHD for many years, and one of the great things is that the children had so much fun while learning the therapeutic abilities they needed to be successful. Play therapy did not feel like "work" to them (even though they were learning and there are specific techniques being applied), and they were eager to engage in therapeutic play or game play therapy to help them towards their goals. As you can imagine, it is much harder to teach a 5-year-old child while they sit on a couch and talk to a therapist for an hour. Frankly, it would be downright boring and difficult for a 5-year-old to engage in a typical talk therapy session anyway. So, make sure to look for a therapist that has experience in play therapy if you have a preschool or elementary schooler (some younger middle school children can benefit from game play therapy as well).

In individual therapy, you will want to make sure that the treatment plan is customized to meet the needs of your child. Do not get a "cookie cutter" treatment plan for a child with ADHD. Instead, work with your therapist on a plan that will help your child with the area they are struggling in most, which may be hyperactivity, impulsivity, social skills, or an attention and concentration problem, which may or may not be combined with depression, anxiety, problems with self-esteem, or another condition. Work with your therapist on a timeline. In some cases, a 12-week plan may be established in the beginning, or it may take more or less time, depending on the reason for therapy services.

Cognitive behavioral therapy is often one type of therapy that can be used for children with ADHD. According to the American Academy of Child & Adolescent Psychiatry, "Treatment for ADHD comes in the form of medication and psychotherapy treatment. Both can be important elements of a comprehensive treatment plan. There are several psychotherapies that are helpful for children with ADHD. We have the most evidence that cognitive-behavioral therapy (CBT) and behavioral management techniques can be helpful for children with ADHD".[31] Cognitive behavioral therapy, also known as CBT, works on dealing with a child's cognitions, or thoughts, as well as helping deal with the behaviors. Sometimes, therapeutic homework will be given to your child, to help them work on their goals between sessions. CBT is often a helpful treatment modality when other conditions are involved in the treatment process as well, such as depression or anxiety, for example.

Behavioral management is another way to treat ADHD. You may work with your therapist on ways to improve your child's behavior, which may include behavior charts for at home and/or at your child's school. In some cases, with your written consent, you can give your therapist permission to speak with your child's teacher and discuss a behavior plan that works best for your child at school.

Often, a reward system is established for your child. When establishing a reward system, it is critical that the "rewards" are actually something that your child wants to earn. I have seen behavior charts not work in the past because the rewards did not match what the child wanted. For example, when a child is being rewarded with stickers and candy, they may quickly get bored (although to some children this would be a great joy). Other children are more highly motivated by extra time to play, extended bedtimes on the weekend, and special time with parent, or getting an inexpensive toy. Know what would be the most motivating reward for your child. Let them make a "wish list" of the rewards they want to earn. Of course, when they list unrealistic items, like going to a theme park or getting a video game, those much larger items might be earned over time, but they must also understand the difference between daily rewards and weekly rewards. Another issue to consider with behavior charts are that the rewards have to be appropriate for the behavior. Smaller, more frequent, rewards are generally recommended for younger children; while larger, less frequent, rewards can be utilized for older children. When it comes to older children, generally middle school age and older, contracts tend to work better for them. The contract should focus on the behavior you would like to see, as opposed to the behavior you do not want to see. The contract should have clear rewards and consequences, and the contracts should have time limits, when appropriate. For instance, if they are working to earn a larger item, the contract should spell out whether they need to have the behavior for a certain report card grading period, for instance. Understood.org has some sample behavioral contracts for younger children, tweens, and teens.[32] Most important of all, for behavior charts or contracts, be clear in your expectations of your child (and realistic!) and remember, you can always revise your plans.

Family therapy

When you hear family therapy, you may think to yourself, why would we need family therapy when it is my child who has ADHD? The reality is that, in some cases, you may also be experiencing family conflict, problems communicating with your child because of ADHD, or you may need some sessions to address family stress that has come up as a result of your child's behavior. With family therapy, it is also important to find a therapist who connects with you and your family. You will want someone who is looking after the best interests of the family and is not necessarily "choosing sides." If your therapist is too "pro-parent," then your child may feel resentful and not feel understood or heard, which can damage the therapist-client relationship. If your therapist is too "pro-child," you may not feel like the therapist is looking out for your best interests as a parent. So, find someone with experience in family therapy situations, and always ask for the therapist's background and their views on the family therapy process, to make sure you have a good fit.

Something to consider with family therapy is who needs to attend. There is no 'one size fits all' family therapy session. Some family sessions may be two parents and several children. Some sessions may be only you and your child. Some sessions can focus on sibling conflict or other sibling matters. It is important to discuss with the therapist who should be in the session. Who is considered family will vary from one family to the next, so think about who is most important in your child's life and how to proceed. Sometimes grandparents, step-parents, aunts, uncles, and other members of the family are very involved, and they may or may not be present in the household setting. Talk to your mental health professional and work together to come up with a list of who will be attending the sessions.

Couples therapy

If you are in a relationship and co-parenting, you may find that raising a child with ADHD can be stressful at times. Indeed, parenthood has its own set of challenges, but raising a child with ADHD requires more patience, more knowledge, and a greater determination to protect your child from society's misunderstanding of their behaviors. Sometimes, these struggles lead to couples conflict, where the stress level affects your relationship. I have seen over the years how the couple raising the child needs interventions as well, sometimes aimed toward reducing the stress of the relationship, as well as sometimes being on board with the co-parenting objectives. It is really stressful for any child to receive mixed messages from different parents. If one parent is more "understanding" of their child's ADHD needs, it can end up being an issue of a "good cop/bad cop" mentality that your child gets into. Similarly, if one parent clearly favors another child without ADHD and treats them very differently, as opposed to the other parent who tries to overcompensate by spending more time with the child with ADHD, this dynamic can create tension on the parenting unit.

You and your partner may also be experiencing other stressors, such as finances, chores, work schedules, intimacy issues, personal problems, which is compounded by your child's ADHD diagnosis. Unfortunately, I have seen some couples where one parent does not believe in the diagnosis or they are in denial about the problem their child has, which can negatively impact the relationship. I have also seen where couples argue because of differences in opinions about whether or not to seek counseling for their child or whether their child should take medication. Additionally, you may be having difficulties in your parenting with one parent being overly organized and structured, while the other parent is not very structured. In this manner, you may see your child respond differently, depending on which parent they are spending time with at the moment. Remember, in general, children with ADHD thrive in structured environments.

So, what can couples therapy do for your relationship? First, couples therapy can be helpful in providing communication tools when it comes to co-parenting. Therapy can also work to uncover any other stressors that may be interfering in your relationship and work to decrease your stress level by providing additional information. Sometimes it is helpful for the parent "in denial" or having a hard time accepting the ADHD diagnosis to speak with their significant other while other mental health professionals are present. I have had some parents say, "Please, I need you to explain to my spouse that my child does have ADHD, because they don't believe me." Upon results of a psychological evaluation, I've had conversations where I have had to tell parents that their child does have ADHD. But, I have also had parents that were convinced that their child had ADHD because of comments from family members or teachers, but upon obtaining the test data, the results showed that their child did not have ADHD, but instead had some other condition. Either way, consulting with another professional or engaging in couples therapy can be one method of receiving help for you and your partner, which ultimately can help your family.

Individual therapy for parents

You might be thinking, 'But I'm not in a relationship. I'm a single parent.' While there are no two families that are alike, sometimes being a single parent brings additional stressors simply because there is one less income, less potential help in the household, and the pressure of raising your child alone. If you have more stress, worry, or tension than you think you can manage, you may think about receiving your own individual therapy. Working on a better 'you' can only help to decrease your stress level and make you a better parent.

> *Working on a better 'you' can only help to decrease your stress level and make you a better parent.*

Think for a moment about your social support network around you. You may be surrounded by supportive grandparents, aunts, uncles, friends, co-workers, friends from places of worship, neighbors, or other individuals invested in you and your child's well-being. For other single parents, they do not feel sufficiently supported. Either way, utilize your resources or increase your level of social support.

How does raising your child with ADHD affect you? Do you feel overly frustrated? Overwhelmed? Angry? Confused? To what level is this stress affecting your own ability to function? Have your emotions impacted your work performance, performance as a parent, or your leisure time? If you have tried various techniques to get back to a healthy emotional state and those strategies are not working, you may need to consider starting individual therapy yourself before you burn out. If you have already hit burn out, then time is of the essence to make sure you are well, too. Children are often very perceptive, so when you are overly stressed and at your wits' end, they truly pick up on that energy and your struggles could impact them negatively.

I have given some examples of being a single parent, since I discussed couples therapy, but individual therapy for parents in a relationship is also very applicable. Sometimes a partner will not be willing to attend couples therapy, or sometimes there is an issue that just one parent needs to sort out at the time. Sometimes, as a parent, you may be more "triggered" by your child with ADHD, for a variety of reasons. Additionally, sometimes parents are grappling with unresolved issues in their own childhood that show up in parenting.

Group therapy

There are several types of group therapy options for your child. One type of group therapy opportunity is a social skills group with same-age peers. While it can be helpful for a child to learn about social communication in a one-to-one setting with a therapist, sometimes the social skills training in individual therapy is not enough. Your child may need more practice at interacting appropriately with same-age peers. Some of the benefits of social skills groups are that your child has an opportunity to actually practice their social skills, like taking turns and sharing (for the younger crowd) or how to communicate strong emotions, what to say to someone that says something negative to them, and how to best communicate their needs. Social skills groups may often have fun activities, especially for the younger children, so check out different social skills groups in your area.

How do you know if your child is a good fit for group? First and foremost, your child should be willing to go to groups. If they are adamant that they do not want to go, it may not be reasonable or feasible to force the process. But, if you know they are being a tad bit reluctant, but will warm up on the first visit, then by all means, encourage the group. Secondly, does your child display anger issues that would be verbally or physically harmful to another child? If so, your child may not be a candidate for a social skills group until they learn how to control their anger around others (an anger management group may actually be more suitable). Thirdly, is your child willing to follow the "rules" of the group leader and put in effort in the group? This can be particularly helpful to lead the transition into a new group, but there are also some fantastic group leaders that can help your child even if they are struggling.

Another type of group is what is called a psychoeducational group; specifically, a group that teaches what ADHD is about, in age-appropriate language. Many of these types of groups work on tools for self-control, organization, planning abilities, and ways to reduce impulsivity. These groups generally are more specific toward ADHD symptoms. One of the things that I love about psychoeducational groups for children with ADHD is that they meet other children with ADHD so they can feel less isolated. Many children feel alone with the diagnosis and feel like they are the only one. With a group that teaches about ADHD in child-appropriate language, it can really help to increase your child's level of social support and understanding of the condition.

There are also parenting groups, where parents of children with ADHD can learn about resources and skills to manage the symptoms of ADHD. Just as how some children have difficulties with feeling alone in the diagnosis of ADHD, many parents have also said they feel alone and as though no other parent in their circle of friends understands what it's like to have a child with ADHD. You may, or may not, know any other parents that have children with ADHD, but either way, sometimes a parent group to increase your support network and learn about more resources can be helpful. You can find a local parenting group at sites like: additudemag.com, chadd.org, parents.com and other searches for your local area.

Chapter 10

Parenting Self-Care

You may be asking yourself, why is there a chapter about self-care for parents in a book about children with ADHD? The truth is that, while you may be searching for answers for your child in this book, one of the "answers" is that you should work on taking care of YOU, too.

Why is Self-Care Important?

Self-care is important for a lot of reasons. Firstly, self-care makes you a better parent. It just does. Would you rather be stressed out and frazzled dealing with the ups and downs of parenting, or would you rather be cool, calm, and collected? Of course, your answer is to be calm. Can you be calm every day? Of course not, but striving for more balance and self-care is a great goal. Secondly, a focus on self-care helps you to be a better role model for your child. In a world of busy-busy-busy, you may be teaching your child that not taking a break is okay. Children with ADHD need to learn self-care skills too, even more so than children without ADHD, because there are often added pressures that come with the diagnosis. So, if you can model taking the time to take care of you, this sets an amazing example for your child. Remember also, that your child needs you to advocate for them. You know your child best. YOU are the expert when it comes to your child. If you are overwhelmed, stressed out, and exhausted, how can you effectively advocate for your child who needs you the most? It makes it a lot more difficult. And lastly,

> *If you are overwhelmed, stressed out, and exhausted, how can you effectively advocate for your child who needs you the most?*

taking the time for your own self-care can really help lead to a healthy family environment. We all know that when a parent is taking care of themselves, it can spread more joy and diminish the stress in a household environment.

No judgment zone

If you are still struggling with guilt associated with having a child with ADHD, I'd like you to realize a few things. First, it is normal for any parent on the planet to have a sense of guilt at times for their child's conditions. But, if your guilt is interfering with your livelihood, productivity, parenting, or relationships, it is time to seek help to reduce your sense of guilt. Focus on forgiving yourself for any parenting mistakes you have made up to this point. We all make mistakes, but most important is moving forward. By reading this book, I am proud of you, because, you are taking the step to help yourself and your child. In fact, just by reading this chapter, it means you have decided not to gloss over this information about ways to take care of yourself. Lastly, be sure to focus on your parenting strengths. I have found that parents have an incredible strength and resilience to get through so much in the world of parenting. Just as you would teach your children to focus on their strengths to boost their self-esteem, it is important that you also give yourself a pat on the back for all you are doing. So, no more pity parties and step into the 'no judgment' zone.

Take a break!

It is so important to just stop and take a break sometimes. There are respite programs available, should you not have anyone who is able to watch your child. Kidshealth.org recommends the following for referrals to respite care below.[33]

- *The Lifespan RespiteCare Program, a federally funded grant program, assists states with improving access to respite care and may provide financial assistance. The program is offered in many states and the District of Columbia. Contact the ARCH National Respite Network and Resource Center to see if there's a program in your state. If not, there might be a State Respite Coalition that can help.*[34]

- *Find private respite programs in your area through the ARCH National Respite Network.*[35] *Tell them what kind of care you need and get a list of providers that may include visiting nurses, childcare centers, and sleepaway camps.*

- *Other groups in your area that may offer respite care include United Cerebral Palsy, Easter Seals, and local chapters of The Arc.*[36,37,38]

A family vacation may be another option for you as a family to take a mental break away from the daily stresses. There are also summer camps specifically available for children with ADHD.[39] No matter which option you choose when taking a break, whether with or without your child, know that there can be many benefits to doing so for your own mental health.

Recharging

Recharging your energy supply source is critical to your self-care process. Make time to exercise! I already know what you're probably thinking: I don't have time! The reality is it's all about our priorities. We make time for so many things, whether it is catching our favorite television shows, social media, or our other hobbies, so we need to make the time for exercise. I am certainly not here to tell you how to exercise, but I am saying to make sure that there is some form of exercise in your weekly routine. There are all sorts of exercise apps now where you can do 30-day challenges at home. There are gym memberships which include childcare. There are running groups, exercise classes, personal trainers, exercises you can do with family, and a combination of the above. Do what you love and what fits your lifestyle, but do find time to exercise.

...give yourself permission to have more fun in your life.

Again, I will remind you that your child needs you to be in your healthiest condition.

Nutrition is of the utmost importance, as well. Make sure to eat healthily to have the energy to take care of your child. Not only does eating healthy help you as a parent, but you are a role model for healthy eating for your child. If you are limiting sugar intake for your child, but often indulging in junk food, what message are you sending to your child? Eating healthy is particularly important for your child's well-being, also.

Make sure to get adequate sleep. You probably hear medical advice all the time, but are you taking the medical advice you often hear regarding sleep? Getting sleep is critical to recharging yourself to ensure that you have enough energy to be the best parent you can be. If you are having trouble sleeping, consider what could be causing your sleep problems. If you need to, follow up with your primary care physician to assess your sleep patterns.

What do you do in your leisure time? Are you finding the time for leisure? It's important to do things that you enjoy, too. It's so easy to concentrate on your children every weekend and their needs, but do you have a hobby that you like to do? Committing to leisure time is important, even if it is a 30-minute period of time each week. Look at your weekly schedule. More than likely, you have work functions, children's appointments, and meetings scheduled, but is your leisure time on your calendar? Schedule it in. Find the time and write it in your planner or put it into your electronic calendar. Again, it is about making the commitment to have time to engage in activities that you enjoy and will make you happy.

Get outdoors! Find an outdoor activity that you love, as well, to help refresh you. There are studies that have shown the benefits of getting outdoors, including improving your mood, better health outcomes, keeping you calmer, and increasing your level of happiness. You can also find activities to do outdoors with your family, like going to the beach, camping, hiking, taking a walk, going to the park, swimming in a pool, or something else that your family loves.

Have fun!

As a parent, you may get so bogged down in the daily life of parenthood that you forget to have fun. Do you remember when you were six years old? Do you remember how exciting things were in your childhood? The joy you had at the simplest things?

We tend to lose our sense of joy as we get older and move into our adulthood years and have to deal with more responsibilities. Despite these things, though, give yourself permission to have more fun in your life. Currently, there are adult coloring books, adult playgrounds, and many more activities for adults to have fun with, as well. You can find a lot of fun activities for parents and family activities to increase the fun factor in your life. There are many organizations that are now offering parent nights out, where you can leave your children for a few hours, which means that they get to have fun while you're having fun, too. Have a great time with a group of friends. Go on a date night if you are in a relationship, or have solo time.

Chapter 11

Advocacy

I have had the opportunity to teach many parents about how to advocate for their child throughout my career, and I have been more than grateful for this opportunity because advocacy is vital for your child. Children often do not have a true voice in society, unfortunately, so parents and caregivers (and the community) have to fill the role of advocating for their needs. When your child has been diagnosed with ADHD, it is even more important to advocate for your child because of the many stereotypes and misconceptions that still exist about ADHD.

Be your child's advocate

If you don't advocate for your child, then who will? I'd like you to stop reading and take a moment to think about that question. The truth of the matter is, that children, especially the younger ones, often have difficulties asserting themselves or have a lack of knowledge about their ADHD symptoms. One of your many roles as a parent is to educate others about your child. To truly advocate effectively, though, you need to remember to always be prepared! While I am grateful that you are reading this book, I hope that you will also go the extra mile for your child and continuing reading books and articles about ADHD to further your understanding of ADHD, the latest trends, and the resources to best help your child to be successful in life. One great way to keep updated on information is to stay informed via newsletter and online communities. Children and Adults with Attention-Deficit/Hyperactivity Disorder (CHADD) is one example of a non-profit organization that has newsletters, online forums, training sessions, and a variety of resources to help parents.[40]

Teaching others about your child

There will be many situations throughout your child's life where you will need to speak up on their behalf. Whether you have just recently learned that your child has ADHD or you have known for many years, you will inevitably have to discuss your child's condition at some point. You may be in situations where you have to explain your child's symptoms to teachers, babysitters, coaches, family members, or other individuals who interact with your child on a frequent basis.

With respect to teachers, also remember that you cannot assume that your child's teacher will understand your child's unique symptoms. Just because another child has ADHD in your child's teacher's classroom does not mean that your child exhibits the same symptoms, and this is something that you must express to your child's teacher. Many parents have asked me whether or not they should share that their child has ADHD with the school system. The answer is highly dependent upon a lot of factors, but generally, it is best to let your child's teacher know what is going on with your child so that they know how best to help them.

If you don't advocate for your child, then who will?

What if you have a new sitter for your child? Are they aware of your child's needs? Since ADHD can express itself in many ways, help the new sitter get to know what works best for YOUR child. Give them the tools and tips necessary for them to understand the triggers so that they can minimize any behavioral incidents. Just as with any sitter and child situation, let your sitter know what the expectations and rules are for your household and what appropriate consequences should be. Lastly, make sure that your sitter has the appropriate expectations for your child, so that they are not getting into trouble for something they can't control, like displaying impulsivity, hyperactivity, or attention issues.

If your child is involved in a sport, you may consider having a conversation with your child's coach. Now, remember, not every child with ADHD has problems in sports, of course, but if your child is struggling with some issue related to their condition, take the time to talk with the coach about some tweaks they might do to make your child's experience better. If you have put some reasonable modifications in place for your child and there is an intense amount of frustration which is too difficult to manage, you may have to consider a different sport. But, keep in mind that pulling your child out of an activity does not have to be the first resort. Things to consider are the type of sport, your child's level of interest, and the number of other children involved, their maturity level, their ability to handle the wins and losses associated with sports, and their ability to manage their symptoms to function appropriately in the sport.

> *The bottom line is this: do what is best for your child and find people that will be supportive of you.*

With respect to family, there may often be extended family that will learn about your child's ADHD symptoms. Some may well be supportive, but other family may be critical of many factors, such as the very diagnosis of ADHD, your parenting skills, whether or not your child should get therapy, and discussing your child with other family members. The bottom line is this: do what is best for your child and find people that will be supportive of you.

Connect with family members that will support you in the process of parenting a child with ADHD. For those family members who are more critical of you, be prepared to set appropriate boundaries with those individuals and advocate for doing what is best for your children.

Know who to contact

Throughout your child's life, you will need to know where to go to advocate for your child. The Department of Education has a guide to navigating through where to go and whom to contact should you have an issue with the public education system. You can utilize school resources, the school principal, and the ESE team in school settings. In some cases, you may wish to have a disability advocate help you advocate for your child in a variety of settings. If your child is an older teen with a job, you can also help to advocate for your child in an employment setting. There are accommodations your child can receive in their job, due to ADHD symptoms that may be impacting their occupational functioning.[41]

Speak to a legislator

Another thing you can do to help not just your child, but all youth with ADHD, is to advocate legislatively. Advocating for new or changes in legislation is often easier than you may think. While I have been very fortunate to advocate for different legislation affecting psychologists and the patients of mental health in my state capital, Tallahassee, as well as federal legislation in Washington, D.C., you don't need to travel (unless you want to) to make a difference legislatively. There are many letters that you can send to your city, state, and federal legislators via email or the postal service to express your views on raising a child with ADHD and what is most effective or needed. CHADD has a great advocacy manual with sample letters for legislators, fact sheets, as well as information about the process of advocating legislatively.[42]

ADHD Awareness month

You can also get involved in local or national efforts to advocate for youth with ADHD. Every October, there are various walks, family events, donation drives, and other events throughout the country for children and families with ADHD. Should your local community not have an event, you may consider hosting your own event. CHADD also has an ADHD Awareness Walk Toolkit to get information on hosting your own walk/run.[43] Another way you can advocate for ADHD is to spread information on social media or word of mouth with family and friends. When you hear of great events, share the information with others, perhaps other families in your social network who also are looking for resources for ADHD, or you may share with friends and families who are supportive in helping others in general with ADHD. I have found that many members of the community are often very supportive and want to help, but simply may not have the information. This is where you come in, so share resources and opportunities for others to advocate to help youth with ADHD. In the end, you are helping to better your child's life and the lives of many others.

Chapter 12

Alternative Treatments for ADHD

I've often heard parents ask, "Is there anything else besides medication and therapy that can help my child with ADHD?" The answer is, sort of. What do I mean by that? Well, there are several alternative treatments that you may have heard of or read about on the internet that suggest treatments that may be helpful for treating ADHD. While some alternative treatments may be helpful, it is important to remember that it is not a cure. Think control, rather than cure.

Yoga

When most people think of yoga, they think of someone with amazing flexibility and I've often heard people say, "It's too hard", or people are afraid to start the practice. However, yoga has been shown to have beneficial effects for kids, too! For starters, yoga is a practice that focuses on deep breathing and utilizes mindfulness techniques. Many children with ADHD can benefit from learning how to focus on their breath and increasing their awareness in the present moment. So, yoga is not just about flexibility.

I was honored and thrilled to speak at the National Kids Yoga Conference in Virginia in October 2017 to talk about how beneficial yoga can be for the emotional health of children. While yoga is certainly not a "cure" for ADHD, think about yoga as another tool in your toolkit as a parent, should you and your child be open to yoga as a form of treatment. Your child may not even need to engage in a full class, but doing some poses at home can be helpful.

> Think control, rather than cure.

LiveStrong.com referenced Yoga Journal in an article on ADHD children and yoga: "According to the 'Yoga Journal,' because forward bends lengthen and deepen each breath, they increase calming exhalations. Such restorative poses as savasana, in which the child lies in a supine position and relaxes every muscle in the body, and viparita Karani, in which the child places legs straight up the wall while resting in a supine position, can bring your child peace of mind."[44] Thus, there are different poses designed for various purposes, but overall, yoga can be a great resource to work on calmness and improving self-control. Yoga is best suited for children who are interested or curious about the practice, or they may want to practice some poses at home. If they are adamant that they do not want to try yoga, do not force them. It's not worth it. Remember to pick your battles wisely.

Meditation

Meditation can also serve as a great calming technique for your child. There are "guided meditations" that you can do with your child. The Chopra Center has some great examples of child-friendly guided meditations.[45] The great thing about guided meditations is that you can participate with your child, especially if they are younger in age. You can find some special time one-on-one with your child and read them a guided meditation script while they close their eyes and work on their relaxation skills. Should they not want you to read the script to them, there is also the option for your child to record themselves reading the script onto a device where they can play the audio afterward. There are meditations that include mantras and there are some that don't, and there are actually a variety of different types of meditations out there. Choose a meditation style that resonates with you and one that you think your child will enjoy. The goal is to help them reduce their hyperactivity, focus on remaining calm, and visualizing calmness. It may be helpful for you to also do visualization techniques with your child to help them visualize positive outcomes for themselves, whether it be at school, home, or extracurricular activities. Many children have found meditation to helpful, and remember, it does not have to be a long and laborious process; but instead, meditation can be completed in short increments. Find a time that works for you and your child.

Special diets

There have been some suggestions over the years that parents of children with ADHD should change their diets. Elimination and various fad diets have been recommended to treat ADHD symptoms. Currently, research does not support that any special diets cure ADHD. There is some research that has shown that omega-3 fatty acids are deficient in some children with ADHD, hence, omega-3 fatty acid supplements may be helpful to reduce some symptoms, but the research is still mixed. There are some families that have tried to eliminate healthy foods to reduce their child's ADHD symptoms. Be careful with playing with your child's nutrition and consult with a physician and/or dietician before making significant meal plan changes.

What about sugar, you ask? Well, according to WebMD, increased sugar intake has not been linked as a cause for ADHD.[46] The site further explains that the reason why some children may be hyper with increased sugar is that the sugar increases their blood sugar level temporarily, giving them more energy. Nonetheless, some parents have found that decreasing junk food and candy has been helpful to reduce "sugar highs" and increased hyperactivity, in addition to ADHD symptoms. There are some pediatricians who do believe that vitamin deficiencies can be linked to ADHD symptoms. Overall, be sure to check with your medical team to consult on this issue. As the research is ongoing, there may always be new developments in coming years.

...meditation can be completed in short increments.

Brain training

One school of thought is that due to the working memory problems for children with ADHD, they need to be trained on how to most efficiently use their brains. You may have heard of many "brain training" games on the market, which most research has not pointed to as a "cure" for ADHD. However, some children are receiving neurofeedback, which chadd.org explains as:

> *"Neurofeedback, formerly called electroencephalographic (EEG) biofeedback, and occasionally referred to as neurotherapy, is an intervention for ADHD based on findings that many individuals with ADHD show low levels of arousal in frontal brain areas, with excess of theta waves and deficit of beta waves. Supporters of this treatment suggest that the brain can be*

trained to increase the levels of arousal (increase beta waves and reduce theta waves) and thereby reduce ADHD symptoms. Neurofeedback treatment involves placing electrodes on a person's head to monitor brain activity. Feedback is given to the patient with cues that can be as simple as an audio beep or as complex as a video game. When the brainwaves are of the desired frequency, the beep may inform the patient, or the character in the game will move in the proper direction. When the patient has learned how to increase these arousal levels, proponents believe improvements in attention will result and that there will be reductions in hyperactive/impulsive behavior."[47]

Discuss with your medical team whether neurofeedback could be beneficial for your child. There are various factors to consider in treatment options with ADHD, so it is best to schedule a consultation to see the advantages and disadvantages for your situation and make the best-informed decision about the treatment modality.

Exercise

Exercise can be a very positive supplement to the other methods of treatment your child is receiving. While some resources have simply stated "just get the child outside to play," the data shows the issue of just "getting the energy all out" is a bit more complex. Nonetheless, getting your child outdoors has shown to have positive outcomes, like improving their mood and reducing their stress levels. You can choose to enroll your child in an active extracurricular activity, such as dance, basketball, swimming, martial arts, or soccer, for example. You and your child's team will need to assess their social abilities and what type of activity may be best for them. You could also decide to engage in some physical activities as a family, such as going to the park, playing a sport together, skating, and hiking together. Overall, though, exercise is a healthy way for your child to work on being emotionally and physically well.

The CDC.gov gives some examples of modeling positive physical activity:

- Lead an active lifestyle yourself.
- Make family time physical activity time. Build physical activity into your family's daily routine. Take a walk after dinner together or do housework or yard work together.
- Use local, low-cost, or free places like public parks, baseball fields, and basketball courts to be active.
- Attend family nights or other physical activity events at your child's school or local community centers.
- Be active whenever possible. Walk or ride bikes to school or the bus stop instead of riding in a car. Parents of young children can enjoy the walk or bike ride, too.
- Include physical activity breaks in events such as long car trips, vacations, or visits to

relatives or friends. Bring along beach balls, bikes, jump ropes, or other items that can be used for active play.[48]

There are many more alternative treatments not included in this book. Remember, there are many alternative treatments that are not fully supported by research, but some treatments may be helpful as supplemental items. Just as if you would not expect one self-help book to solve all of your problems, you should not expect one alternative treatment to fully resolve your child's ADHD. Consult with your resources and always continue to explore your options.

Chapter 13

Conclusion
or What's Next

Now that you have learned more about the components of ADHD, what a comprehensive psychological evaluation can do to review your diagnosis of ADHD, the accommodations your child may receive, and what to do in terms of intervention, you will want to make a plan.

The importance of a team

One of the most important things you can do for your child is to create a team approach. Your team should consist of the pediatrician, mental health professional, psychiatrist (in some cases), any other necessary specialists, the academic team, and parental support (friends, family, etc.). In the healthcare world, you may wish to give consent to have your child's medical records released among different healthcare providers. Be sure to follow up to see if your child's physician(s) and mental health care professionals are communicating about what your child needs most. Additionally, sometimes it's helpful for your mental health professional to be in contact with your child's teacher or the school. Your team members may also include a larger or smaller number of people, but the most important thing is the collaboration of all the individuals working together for the best interest of your child. Also remember that YOU are on this team, as well.

Once you have your team in place, be sure to follow up to make sure communications are occurring that should be occurring. If your teacher has agreed to speak to the academic team about 504 plan changes, for instance, be sure to follow up. If your mental health professional has agreed to follow up with sending a report to your child's physician or vice versa, follow up. Most cases work best when everyone is aware of who is on the "team" to best help your child.

ADHD does not define your child

Something to always remember is that ADHD does not define your child. Remind your child of their strengths and teach your child what ADHD is and what it is not. Now that you have the knowledge base you need, make a commitment to continue learning about ADHD, and teach your child in age-appropriate language about the changes with ADHD. Remember, you also have a team of professionals to answer your questions and help in explaining anything to your child that you need to.

Love your child unconditionally

It's important to stress that your child needs your support always. Empower them by helping them to learn strategies at home and coping with any struggles that they may have. Find ways to always continue supporting them through this journey, and help them find their own support system. While you may prefer for your child to lean on you, remember that they will not be in your sight 24/7, so they must learn ways to rely on themselves and others. Help them to find supportive individuals in their life, whether it be peers, teachers, coaches, other family members, etc.

Utilize your resources

Reach out! Do your own research, but also reach out to the professionals on your team. In other words, use your resources wisely. You may be part of a non-profit organization that supports ADHD, a support group online or in person, or a therapeutic team; either way, be sure to reach out. I've found that parents have said they have thought of questions at home, but forgot them by the time they reached my office. Thus, what some parents have done is they've jotted down their questions on a notepad to bring to the appointment. I really love to see preparation from a parent because I know that parent is going to get their questions answered.

Change your expectations

Remember in the home setting to make the necessary changes discussed in the prior chapters. Help everyone in your family to change something about them for the better, so as not to isolate your child as the "problem child" or the one who is "different." And remember, try not to make it obvious that you are comparing your child with ADHD to your child without ADHD. While it's normal for many parents to compare siblings, do so in your mind, versus making comparative statements aloud. Saying things like, "James never can do his homework like you can, because his ADHD gets in the way" or something to that effect can make your child with ADHD feel inferior. There are statements that you may say that can truly affect your child's self-esteem unintentionally. So, choose your words wisely.

Patience and frustration

The next thing to think about is patience. Please, remember to be more patient with your child with ADHD, because there are some things that are outside of their control. When they say things like, "I just can't help it", sometimes that statement is actually true. I have met many children that struggle so much and want so badly to do well and please their parents and their teachers, but they are struggling with hyperactivity, impulsivity, and self-control. It is just heartbreaking when parents and teachers unintentionally require unrealistic expectations. So, remember to be more patient with your child. It can make a world of difference. Am I saying to not have high expectations for your child? Of course, not. But, I am saying to make your expectations realistic and be patient with them and understand, especially if you're at the beginning of this journey, that it's a learning process not just for you as a parent but for also for your child. So, give them the opportunity to learn the strategies to help themselves in life, which they can do through therapy, social skills groups, and what you teach them at home.

Create a team approach.

The other piece to really think about is to also be patient with yourself. You cannot expect to learn everything that you want to learn about ADHD overnight. We all know that's absolutely impossible. I've had the opportunity to interview hundreds of children and teenagers with all sorts of different mental health conditions, and I have seen so many children that are struggling and they want so badly for their parents to understand them, so be patient with yourself. This is a process. The best thing about developing more patience for yourself and setting realistic expectations is that it helps you in the process of learning how to best help your child. Your child absolutely needs you. I can tell you that one of the major things that I hear is that children want to be understood. They want to be understood by their peers. They want to be understood by their parents. They want their parents to love them for who they are. They want their parents to have realistic expectations.

It is also important that you recognize where your frustration level is with your child. I have never met a parent in my life that has not had some type of frustration. So one of the things that you have to do is not only help your child, but you have to learn to control your own frustration that is likely to happen when your child is hyperactive or when your child is being impulsive and doing things they shouldn't be doing in school, for instance. What do you need to do as a parent to make sure that you are working on your own level of frustration? Do you need to take a "parent time out"? In other words, do you need to step away from the situation when you're aggravated by something as to not make the situation worse? Do you need to count to ten? Do you need to take more of your own self-care time to think about all the things that you need to do and work on those things?

Calming activities

Calming activities can vary. For some children, they love arts and crafts. What are the things that they really like to do? Do they like to paint? Do they like to just take a break and watch television?

Do they like to engage in some type of brain game, something fun, or do they like to be outside and take a leisurely walk with you? Believe it or not, I have met many children that just love to go on a walk with their families, take their dog for a walk, or spend some time with their cat or other pet in their room. Many children love animals, so spending time with animals may be going to an animal shelter if they're older and volunteering, or maybe just really taking the time to find something that is very calming for your child.

> *There are statements that you may say that can truly affect your child's self-esteem unintentionally. So, choose your words wisely.*

Now, another piece of this is to really think about what is calming for you. So, again, that varies quite a bit. Personally, I've been a fan of yoga ever since I was in graduate school because it's such a calming activity in our busy world. We often don't really find the time to have calming activities, so it's really important to find that calm time for yourself. For some parents, they decide to take 15 minutes out of their day, every day, and just take a moment, even if they have to lock themselves in a bathroom. Even if you find some calming minutes when you take a shower or brush your teeth, just take a moment to enjoy a couple of deep breaths.

Never stop learning

I cannot stress this enough. Never stop learning about ADHD, because life changes and your child's needs will be different in elementary, middle, high school, and post high school. Their needs will be different in school, emotionally, physically, and mentally. Like any child, your child with ADHD will require a different you, depending on the stage of their life, but the difference is that having a child with a disability can sometimes come with more challenges, and they need your help to learn how to navigate through the tough times. Your child needs your help understanding cyberbullying, the stereotypes that some people have about ADHD, the accommodations they may need in their classroom, and how to approach the world. Sometimes, older children are embarrassed about using their accommodations of extra time on tasks, for example, because they fear what other students may think of them. Thus, teaching your child to be emotionally healthy and strong can lead to them being able to manage their thoughts about having different needs.

Remember the five steps for understanding ADHD we covered in Chapter 2. You may not be at step one or two or three, but you may be dealing with how to cope with the confirmation that your child has ADHD, or you may be in the intervention stage, as well. I recognize that there are many children who also have other needs which may necessitate speech therapy, occupational therapy, a sensory processing condition, an auditory processing condition, or various other mental or physical health conditions. So, in that case, there may be more specialists that you will have to work with and that is why collaboration is so important. But remember above all else to continue to take action, continue to always strive to keep hope for your child, and remember to always advocate for your child. Your child needs you so much.

Chapter 14

A Personal Note

I don't know exactly what your particular reason was for reading this book. I can only assume you have a loved one who has been diagnosed with ADHD or you work in the field and came looking for more answers. Either way, I applaud you for taking the time to advance your knowledge so that you could be a blessing to someone else. I hope you now have a better understanding of what your child or someone with ADHD is going through.

It has been a tremendous honor and a privilege to work in the field of mental health. There are so many barriers at this time and the stigma is still strong, but I am elated to be in this field and also to advocate along with you in the field of mental health. So, don't stop believing in the process of getting your child help. You are fortunate to live in a digital age where you can have access to plentiful information to make your child successful.

You have many opportunities to go to websites to reach out to individuals online. There are so many different resources, camps, programs and therapists, and all sorts of really great, amazing interventions for your child with ADHD and they're all just an Internet search away. This is the digital age we live in, so take advantage of that! Make sure to keep yourself educated.

Make sure to keep reading other books and keep involving yourselves in other activities. Continue to teach your child what they need to know at an age-appropriate level about ADHD. Help them to have the self-esteem that they need to get through a diagnosis with ADHD. There are numerous people that are highly successful with ADHD, but those individuals have learned how to cope with the ADHD symptoms and they have learned what to do with those symptoms to make sure that they are as successful as they can be. Please take advantage of the many resources I have provided at the end of this book.

I wish you the best of luck on your journey. Feel to connect with me on various social media platforms. I would love to hear from you, and I am grateful that you are taking the time to do what is best for your child and family.

If you'd like me to speak at a school, event, function, or on the phone with a family being torn apart by the struggle of coping with ADHD, remember... I'm here to help.

Acknowledgments

There are so many people that I would like to thank in the process of writing this book. First, I would like to thank all of the families that I have worked with over the years for their resilience, strength, and courage while going through the process of best helping their children with ADHD. It has truly been an honor to meet so many outstanding families.

I also want to thank Topher Morrison and Key Person of Influence (KPI) in Tampa for motivating me to "keep going" in the process of writing this book. I have been blessed to be surrounded by a wonderful group of supportive individuals during this process. A huge thank you to Eli Gonzalez and his editing team, as well as Alex Rodriguez, book cover designer and his web development team, as I am truly grateful for their help in establishing this book as a resource.

In doing the research for the resources for this book, finding quality resources to help families with ADHD was wonderful. I'd like to thank all of the organizations and resources that work so hard to provide valuable tools for parents, families, and professionals who work with children with ADHD. Without the research, organizations, facilities, professionals, and advocates we could not have seen as much progress as we have in the field of ADHD, so to everyone, I am grateful.

I would also like to thank my family, friends, and colleagues for all of your support, likes, retweets, and shares on social media of all the postings related to helping children and families. It has been a humbling experience to recognize how fortunate I am to have such a strong supportive network. I genuinely appreciate each and every one of my friends and family members who have helped along the journey of writing this book. Thank you!

Resources

To find more resources, please visit links to websites, books, and ADHD trainings at DrNekeshiaHammond.com.

Sample IEP Form:

| **Individual Education Program (IEP)** |

(Student's Name)   (Date of Meeting to Develop or Review IEP)

Note: For each student with a disability beginning at age 14 (or younger, if determined appropriate by the IEP team), and updated annually, a statement of the transition service needs of the student under the applicable components of the student's IEP that focuses on the student's courses of study (such as participation in advanced-placement courses or a vocational education program).

Present Levels of Educational Performance

Measurable Annual Goals (Including Benchmarks of Short-Term Objectives)

1 of 4

Use of this IEP format, or any other format, will not, in and of itself, ensure compliance with Part B requirements. Whatever or not a State or local agency chooses to require or recomend that teams use this format for IEPs, it is critical that all IEP team participants, including parents, recive clear guidance and training regarding IDEA Part B requirements and the importance of the IEP in focussing instruction to meet the unique needs of each child with a disability.

References

Chapter 2

1 https://www.cdc.gov/ncbddd/adhd/diagnosis.html

2 https://www.cdc.gov/ncbddd/adhd/data.html

3 https://www.mayoclinic.org/diseases-conditions/adhd/symptoms-causes/syc-20350889

4 http://www.aappublications.org/news/2017/02/16/ADHDBrain021617

5 http://www.cnn.com/2017/10/30/health/acetaminophen-adhd-pregnancy-study/index.html

6 https://www.healthline.com/health/adhd/causes#smoking-and-alcohol5

7 "Long-Term Outcomes of ADHD: Academic Achievement and Performance" https://doi.org/10.1177/1087054714566076

Chapter 4

8 https://www.stopbullying.gov/what-is-bullying/index.html

9 https://www.stopbullying.gov/what-is-bullying/index.html

10 https://www.theatlantic.com/health/archive/2014/07/how-childhood-trauma-could-be-mistaken-for-adhd/373328/

Chapter 5

11 "Know Your Rights: Students with ADHD" https://www2.ed.gov/about/offices/list/ocr/docs/dcl-know-rights-201607-504.pdf

[12] "Students with ADHD and Section 504: A Resource Guide" https://www2.ed.gov/about/offices/list/ocr/docs/504-resource-guide-201612.pdf

[13] https://www.additudemag.com/getting-help-for-a-struggling-student/

[14] https://www2.ed.gov/parents/needs/speced/iepguide/index.html#Sample Form

[15] https://www2.ed.gov/parents/needs/speced/iepguide/iepguide.pdf

[16] https://www.understood.org/en/school-learning/special-services/ieps/what-to-bring-to-an-iep-meeting

[17] https://www.therapyshoppe.com/

Chapter 6

[18] http://helpguide.org/

[19] http://www.wrightslaw.com/info/organize.file.htm

[20] https://www.additudemag.com/educational-advocate-adhd-accommodations-legal-help/

[21] https://www2.ed.gov/about/offices/list/ocr/letters/colleague-201607-504-adhd.pdf

[22] https://www.greathomeschoolconventions.com/

Chapter 7

[23] https://huntingtonhelps.com/adhd-tutoring

[24] http://www.pacer.org/bullying/resources/students-with-disabilities/

[25] https://store.samhsa.gov/apps/knowbullying/

[26] http://journals.sagepub.com/doi/10.1177/1087054717734646

Chapter 8

[27] https://www.additudemag.com/download/routines-for-kids-with-adhd/

[28] http://freeprintablebehaviorcharts.com/

Chapter 9

[29] "How to Choose a Psychologist" http://www.apa.org/helpcenter/choose-therapist.aspx

[30] "What to Expect in a Play Therapy Session" http://www.a4pt.org/page/ParentsStagesofThera

[31] http://www.aacap.org/aacap/Families_and_Youth/Resource_Centers/ADHD_Resource_Center/Home.aspx

[32] https://www.understood.org/en/family/managing-everyday-challenges/daily-expectations-child/download-parent-child-behavior-contracts

Chapter 10

[33] "Respite Care for Children with Special Needs" http://kidshealth.org/en/parents/respite-care.html

[34] http://archrespite.org/ta-center-for-respite/state-lifespan-respite-programs

[35] http://archrespite.org/us-map

[36] http://ucp.org/resources/parents-and-families/caregiving/respite-care/

[37] http://www.easterseals.com/our-programs/camping-recreation/respite-services-profile.html

[38] http://www.thearc.org/find-a-chapter

[39] http://www.veryspecialcamps.com/summer/adhd-camps/

Chapter 11

[40] http://www.chadd.org/

[41] https://askjan.org/media/adhd.html

[42] http://www.chadd.org/advocacy/chadd-advocacy-manual.aspx

[43] http://www.chadd.org/Training-Events/ADHD-Awareness-Month.aspx

Chapter 12

[44] https://www.livestrong.com/article/354383-yoga-meditation-for-kids-with-adhd/

[45] http://www.chopra.com/articles/3-kid-friendly-meditations-your-children-will-love#sm.00000543q3rnesev4uqxte4ff0bne

[46] https://www.webmd.com/add-adhd/childhood-adhd/food-dye-adhd#1

[47] http://www.chadd.org/Understanding-ADHD/About-ADHD/Treatment-of-ADHD/Complementary-and-Other-Interventions/Neurofeedback-EEG-Biofeedback-.aspx

[48] https://www.cdc.gov/healthyschools/physicalactivity/toolkit/factsheet_pa_guidelines_families.pdf

About the Author

Dr. Nekeshia Hammond was raised in Orlando, Florida and now resides in the Tampa Bay area with her spouse and 5-year-old son. When not working, she greatly enjoys spending time with her family and learning about the joys of life through the eyes of her young son.

Dr. Hammond is the owner of Hammond Psychology & Associates, a private practice designed to help children, teens, families, and adults. She has over a decade of experience working in the field of psychology. She has also been featured in various TV, radio, and magazines throughout the country, and she is the TV host of Parenting Explained with Dr. Hammond. To *learn more about* the show, visit: www.DrHammondshow.com.

In her spare time, she enjoys reading, yoga, traveling, and serving on boards to help the community. She is the 2018 Immediate Past President of the Florida Psychological Association and serves on the Board of Directors for the Ryan Nece Foundation. She lives by the motto "give back."

For speaking engagements or media consultations, Dr. Hammond can be reached through her website, www.DrNekeshiaHammond.com .

You can also follow her on social media:

Twitter: @DrHammond
Facebook: Dr. Nekeshia Hammond
Instagram: @ADHDexplained

Ingram Content Group UK Ltd.
Milton Keynes UK
UKHW021813080523
421421UK00011B/715